AIRDOGS

VOLUME 1 IN THE DOGFIGHT SERIES

DEDICATED TO THOSE WHO WERE THERE.

I would like to thank some of our wonderful friends for the help they have given us for creating this humble work. Bartek Belgarcz provided invaluable help for avoiding many technical errors, and also on some important historical points. Leah McGovern drew one of the beautiful maps. My friend Jack R gave invaluable help with proof-reading the work at a point when exhaustion meant we were too weary to spot numerous mistakes. Another who gave assistance with the structure of the story was my old friend Andy Salm. Throughout, giving encouragement and support has been George Fanning, particularly through the dark hours when we thought we would never finish. In helping with promotional issues, we are indebted to Will Arnold, and also Michal Holdynski gave us great encouragement as we embarked on the Polish translation. **TIM HOLDEN**

First published in Great Britain 2018 by TH BOOKS

A catalogue record for this book is available from the British Library

ISBN 978-1-9164901-0-9

AIRDOGS : DOGFIGHT VOL 1
Author: Tim Holden
Illustrator: Ivan Fanning

Cover design and print management: Andrew Nadolski

Printed by Brightsea Press, Exeter

www.dogfightnovel.co.uk

AIRDOGS

WRITTEN BY TIM HOLDEN

ILLUSTRATED BY IVAN FANNING

LT VLADEK

A great pilot officer who becomes an air ace.

THE AMERICAN

Friendly and engaging, but what is he up to? And why does he seem to be everywhere?

WALTER

Zan's younger brother, a fierce boy partisan who remains in Poland and becomes a man during the course of the war.

SOPHIE

She is Zan's mother, originally from the Ukraine, and her story is the story of many others.

CAST OF CHARACTERS

RACHEL

A mysterious partisan girl with a story of great importance.

ZAN

A corporal pilot who discovers the price of success in the course of years of fighting.

CORPORAL GLUPEK

Officious and bureaucratic, he's a rare villain and coward as well. He causes an immense amount of trouble.

TEDDY

He's a corporal in 121 Squadron and is Zan's great friend all the way, sticking with him through every trial.

FEBRUARY 2012, ON THE EDGE OF THE INDIAN OCEAN
YOU SHOULD FORGET THIS TASK.
Café
A father speaks to his son

WHY WOULD YOU WANT TO TELL SUCH A STORY?

SO THAT PEOPLE KNOW
NOT JUST ABOUT WHAT YOU DID. BUT SO THAT THEY KNOW WHAT HAPPENED TO EVERYONE

PEOPLE DO NOT WANT TO KNOW. PEOPLE WANT TO FORGET - THEY HAVE FORGOTTEN

UNTIL YOU TROUBLED ME I HAD NEARLY FORGOTTEN.
TELL THE STORY AND LET THEM CHOOSE TO FORGET, IF THEY WILL... GO ON...
They look across the silver sea.
And go back in time...

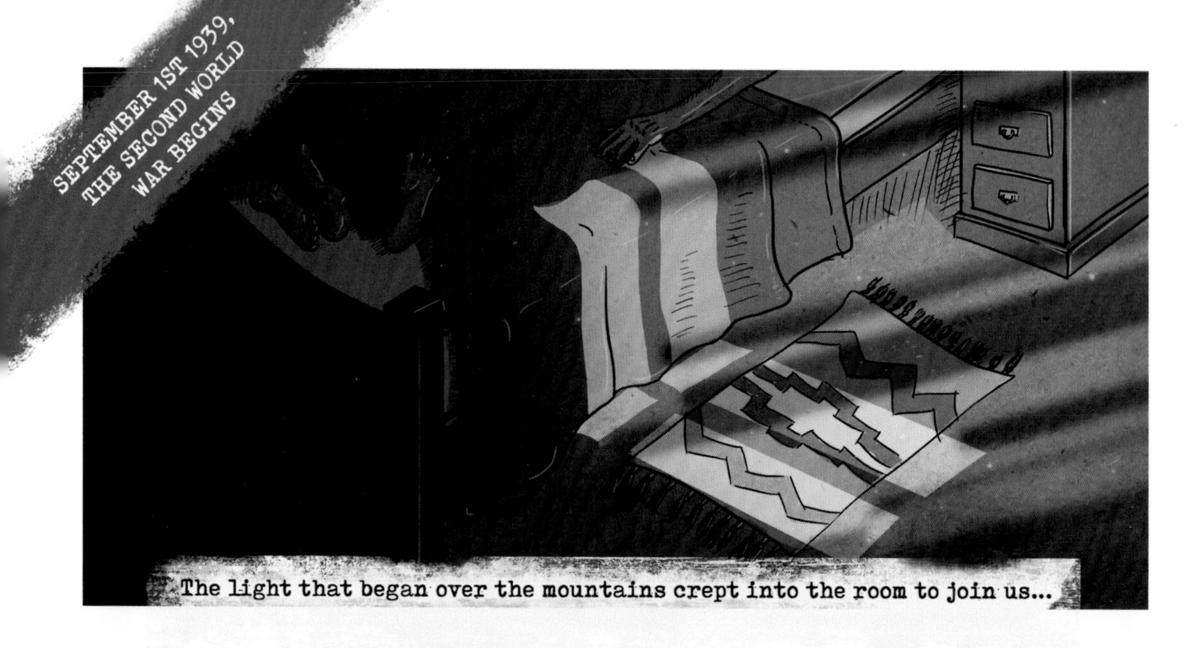
SEPTEMBER 1ST 1939,
THE SECOND WORLD
WAR BEGINS
The light that began over the mountains crept into the room to join us...

A subtle thief who came to steal our dreams where we lay in the dark
wrapped together.

VARRMMMMMMMMMMMMMM

VARRMMMMMMMMMMMM

German Heinkel 111s and Dornier 17s rumbled overhead.
I would never see her again

The airfield had been moved because the attack was expected

It was a long way...

Temporary airfield 121 Squadron

Glupek was a lower rank, but always pretended to be in charge

The engineers rushed

Chocs
were zwipped
CHOCS
ZWIP

VVVHHHRRRRRRR
VVVHHHRRRR
The radial engines fired up
WWHRRRRRRR

The guys were keen

WATCH
OUT!!
But in the rush
two planes collided

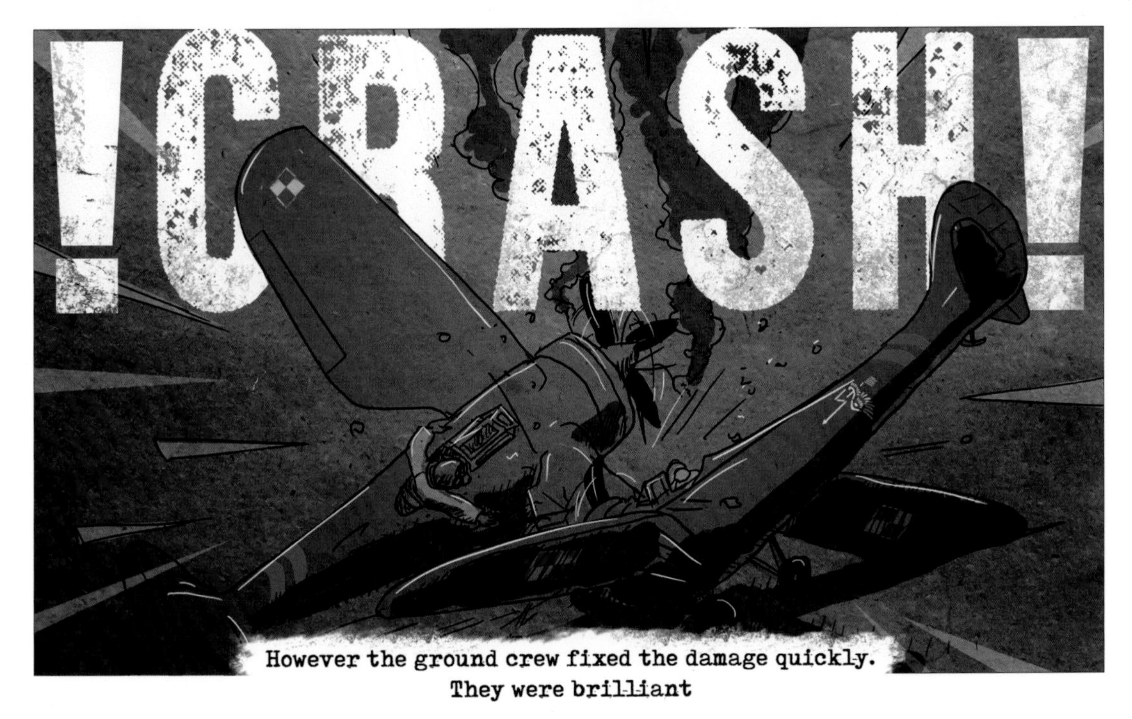
!CRASH!
However the ground crew fixed the damage quickly.
They were brilliant

THAT WASN'T MY FAULT!
Glupek often said this

MEDWECKI! HURRY! BEFORE THE WAR IS OVER
SHUT UP GLUPEK.

Captain Medwecki took off first

But a Stuka dive bomber swept in

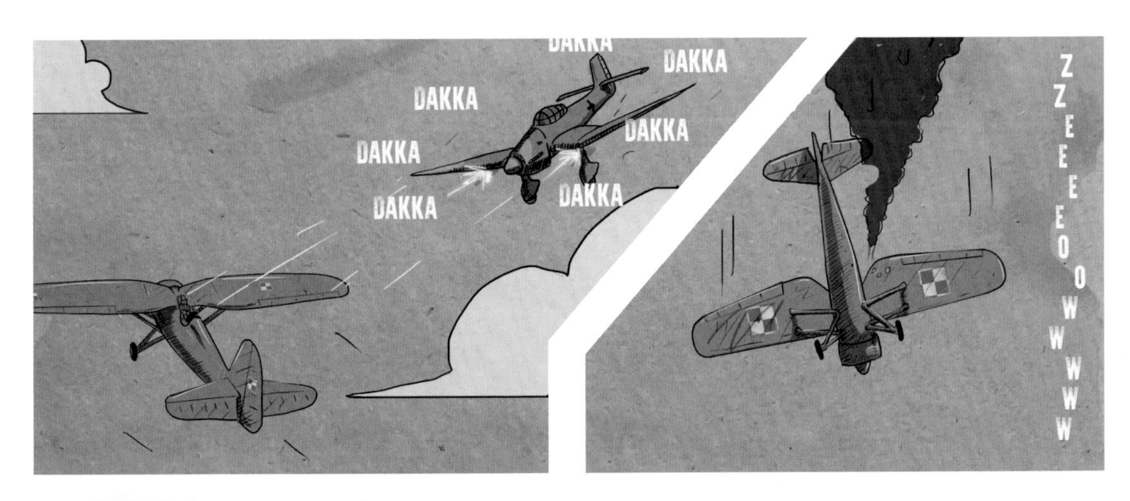
DAKKA
DAKKA
DAKKA
DAKKA
DAKKA
DAKKA
ZZEEEEOOWWWWW

BO OM
OUR CAPTAIN!

INTO THE AIR BOYS!!
Motivation!

Our P.11's took off over the hedge past the smoking wreck

Flying a P.11 is a delicate business
VVRRRRRRRRRRRRRRRRR

It responds to a nudge

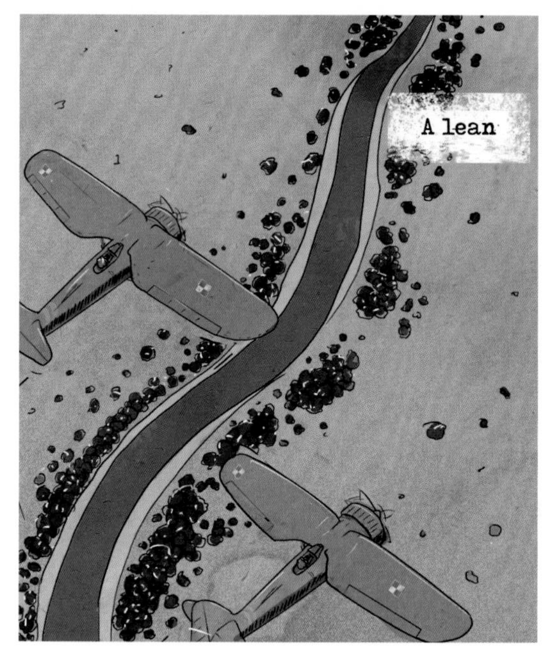
A lean

We scanned the sky as smoke rose over the city's burning railyards

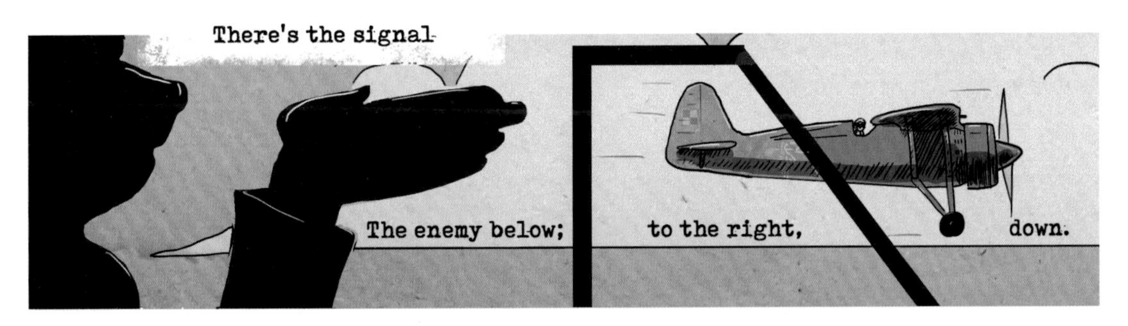
There's the signal
The enemy below;
to the right,
down.

We tried a great sweeping manouvre
But our radial engines pulled us the wrong way
HAHA POLSKI'S

HE'S GETTING AWAY!

DAMMIT!

WE COULDN'T GET THEM...

THE CAPTAIN IS DEAD

AND THE RADIOS DON'T WORK

WE DON'T KNOW WHEN THEY'RE COMING...
AND WE'RE SLOWER THAN THEY ARE

AND WE CAN ONLY CATCH UP TO THEM WHEN WE'RE IN A DIVE

ALRIGHT. THEN WE FIGHT HARDER

REFUEL, RELOAD AND LET'S GET BACK OUT THERE

Glug
Glug
FISSS!

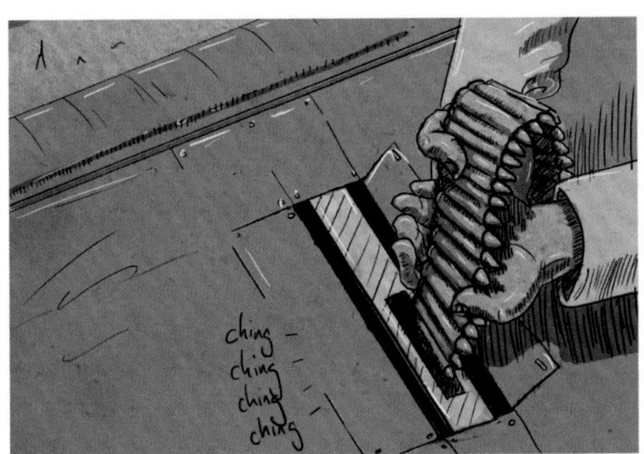
ching
ching
ching
ching

CLITCHK!
The Bristol Mercury engine roared into life

WHIP
WHIP
ZZEEEEOOOWWWW

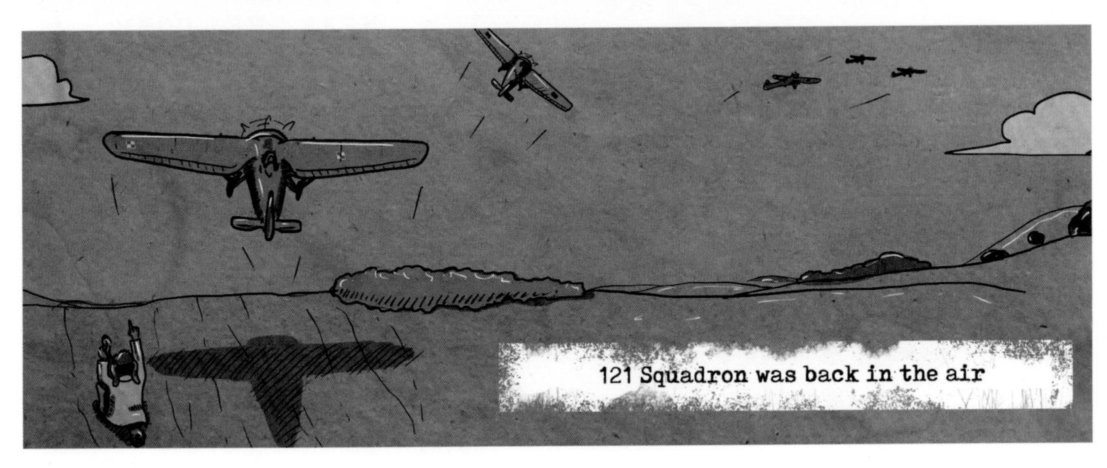
121 Squadron was back in the air

OUTNUMBERED

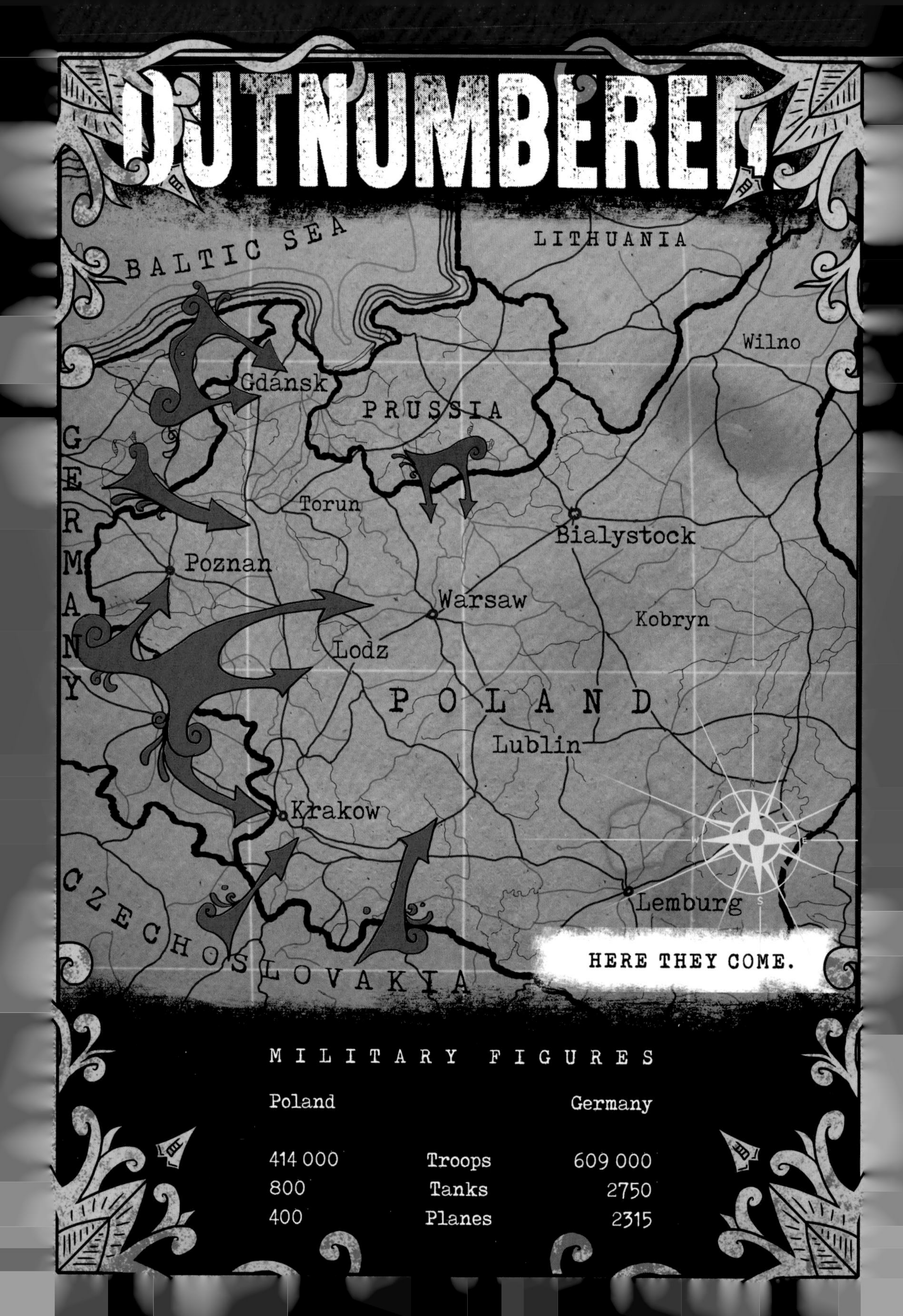

MILITARY FIGURES

Poland		Germany
414 000	Troops	609 000
800	Tanks	2750
400	Planes	2315

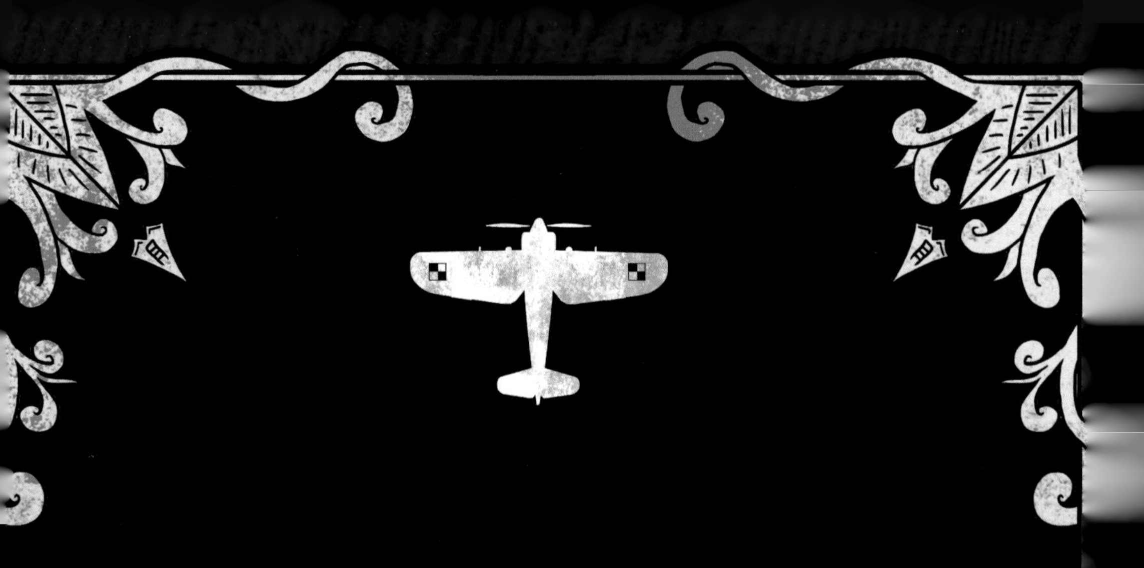

"Death had come across the border. A great spasm would agonise the land for years to come, to steep it in blood. Millions were to die after this first day, uncountable lives were to be cut short without mercy. The merciless obeyed their orders. These orders were spoken, barked out in words. And the unspeakable was then done.

I will not do the dead the disservice of listing statistics of those who died, of how many millions of these folk or those peoples, or of the millions who were brought to Poland to die. They all wanted to live, they all hoped and loved and sometimes laughed, cared about their families and loved their children.

Poland had to fold them into her arms, and take them to the roots within her soil. I am sure the land keeps them still, and soothes them forever.

A shadow had come, invading Poland not only with steel and soldiers but with a great darkness. That shadow sang marching songs as its engines of war tore at our soil. Perhaps the only consolation is that the shadow has maybe faded just a little.

I am now going to tell you of an unarmed man who faced those who came to remove his horses. He, like all those others, was to be wrapped within the soil of the fertile land."

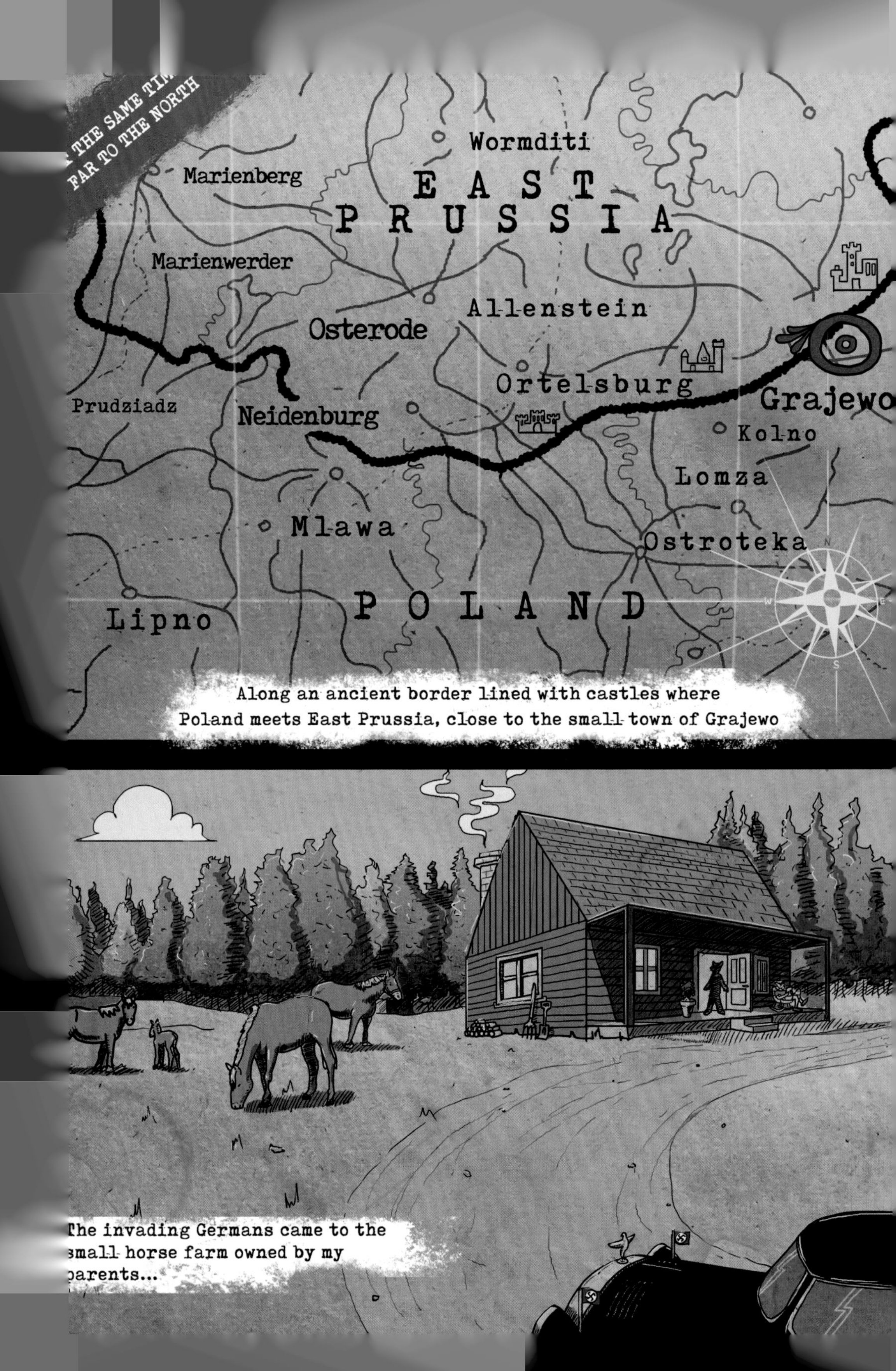
THE SAME TIM
FAR TO THE NORTH
Wormditi
Marienberg
EAST
PRUSSIA
Marienwerder
Allenstein
Osterode
Ortelsburg
Grajewo
Prudziadz
Neidenburg
Kolno
Lomza
Mlawa
Ostroteka
POLAND
Lipno
Along an ancient border lined with castles where
Poland meets East Prussia, close to the small town of Grajewo
The invading Germans came to the
small horse farm owned by my
parents...

SOPHIE,
GET INSIDE!

I WILL MAKE SURE THE HORSES ARE SAFE

WALTER,
MY BOY
He spoke to his younger son, my brother

RUN FOR THE WOODS.

click!
SKRRTTT
YOU, OLD MAN. KEEP WHERE YOU ARE

THESE HORSES ARE NOW THE PROPERTY OF THE REICH

TAKE IF YOU WILL, THE COLTS. BUT NOT THE STALLION AND THE MARES

FOOL! HE IS RESISTING!

SHOOT HIM!

GET THE HORSES.
klop
klop klop
klop klop
Gasp!
VARRMMMMMMMMMMMM
SOPHIE... — I LOVE YOU
I WISH, OUR OTHER BOY WAS HERE...

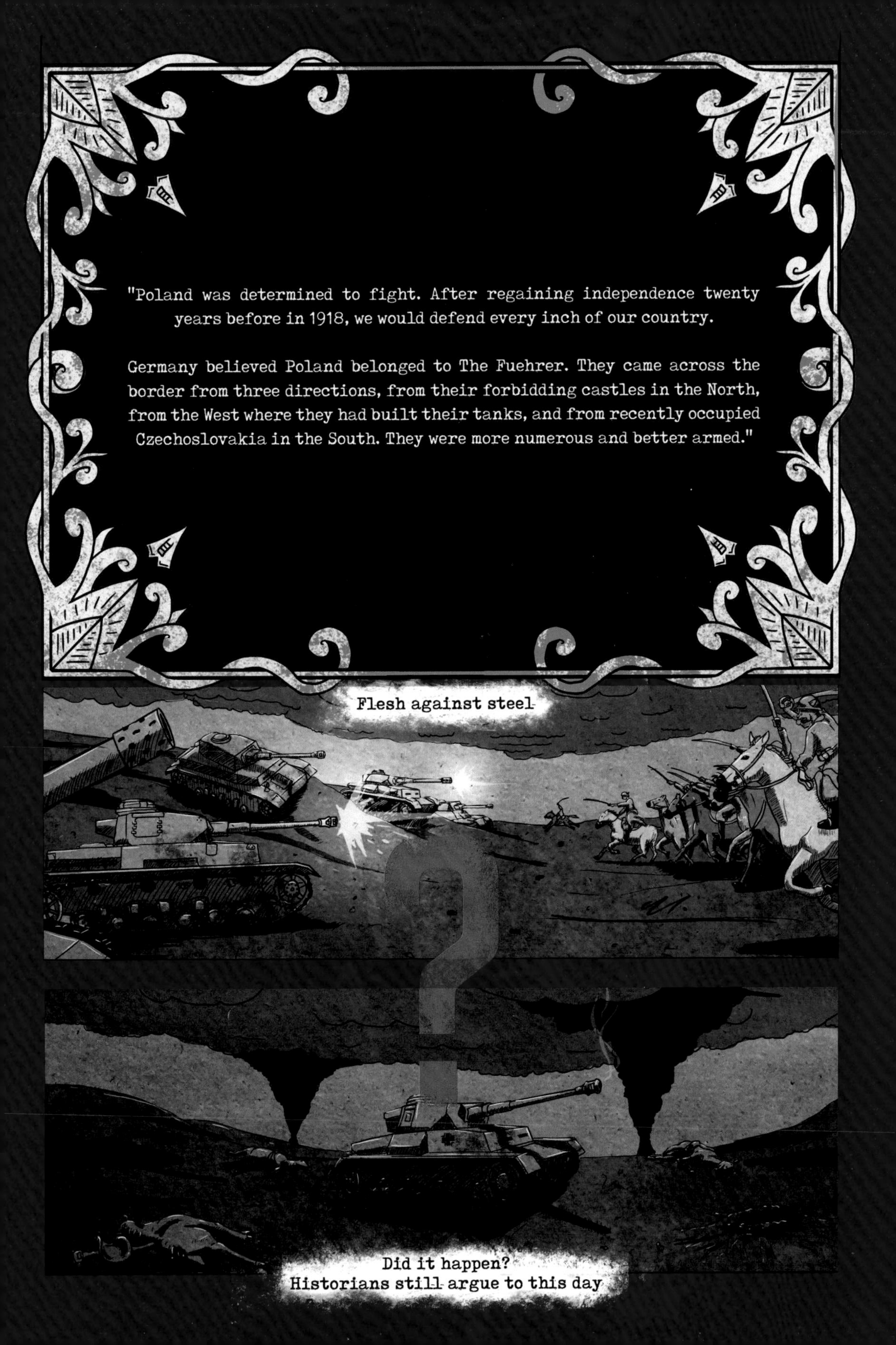
"Poland was determined to fight. After regaining independence twenty years before in 1918, we would defend every inch of our country.
Germany believed Poland belonged to The Fuehrer. They came across the border from three directions, from their forbidding castles in the North, from the West where they had built their tanks, and from recently occupied Czechoslovakia in the South. They were more numerous and better armed."
Flesh against steel
Did it happen?
Historians still argue to this day

"On the 23rd of August, a few days before the invasion, the ambassadors for Russia and Germany met

VEE ARE YOUR FRIENDS!

MORONIC HUN.

YOU ARE OUR FRIENDS, JA AND WE EVEN LIKE YOU, JA

STUPID RUSKI UNTERMENSCH.

MOLOTOV

RIBBENTROP

They were Vyacheslav Molotov and Joachim von Ribbentrop and they were known to despise each other

Little did the Poles know that a secret deal had been made between Hitler and Stalin.
But both of them had plans to destroy one another

NEVER BELIEVE A GERMAN. BUT WE MORE HATE THE POLES. WE WILL DEFEAT THEM, TAKE BACK WHAT THEY HAVE STOLEN FROM US AND THEN START KILLING GERMANS. DA

STALIN

WE WILL GET ZEM TO HELP US TAKE POLAND AND ZEN WE WILL ATTACK ZE RUSSIANS. JA

They kept all this quiet and the Poles did not know

HITLER

THE NIGHT OF THE SAME DAY,
AT THE TEMPORARY AIRFIELD
121
We had just started talking with our new captain

I HEARD GUYS SHOT DOWN TWO OF THEM...

YOU ARE USELESS!

This was the beginning of a massive tragedy. One in five inhabitants of Poland would be dead before the war ended

PEOPLE, PLEASE!

Our new captain spoke

WE GO
INTO THE SKY TO
FIGHT FOR YOU

THE ENEMY IS STRONG, WE
LOST GOOD MEN TODAY BUT
WE TOOK DOWN TWO
OF THEM

AND TOMORROW,
WE FIGHT AGAIN

GO HOME. PROTECT YOUR LOVED ONES AND HELP IN
THE FIGHT FOR OUR SACRED MOTHERLAND

THIS NEW GUY
CAN TALK
MAYBE HE CAN FLY
TOO...

BE READY AT DAWN.

THREE DAYS LATER,
THE KREMLIN
Russia had not attacked yet, despite their pact with Germany

SHOULD I ATTACK POLAND AND KEEP THE COMMITMENT THAT FOOL MOLOTOV GAVE THOSE HATED NAZIS
OR SHOULD I VAIT...
-
VAIT AND SEE IF THE HUNS CONTINUE TO WIN... ? VAIT... VAIT...
Stalin schemed, always cunning and dangerous

CHURCHILL

"On the same day that Britain declared war on Germany, Winston Churchill was brought into Britain's Cabinet as First Sea Lord and put in charge of the naval fleet.

For many years he had been a political pariah, warning a nation exhausted by the Great War that a threat was growing in Adolf Hitler's Nazi Germany. Nobody wanted to listen.

At the age of sixty five he was back in front line politics, unpopular with many, but determined to fulfill what he saw as his destiny."

Several planes had already been lost

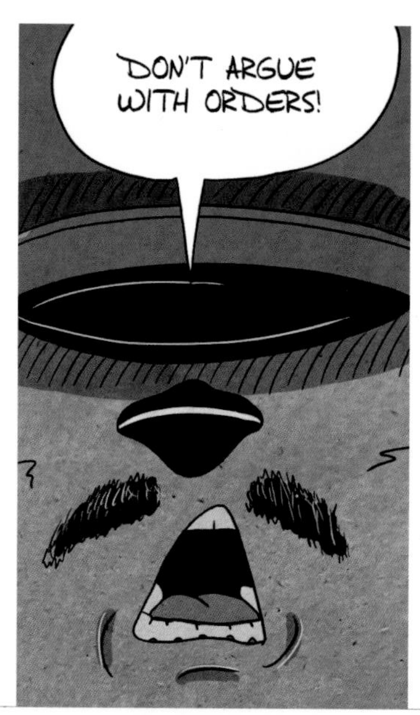

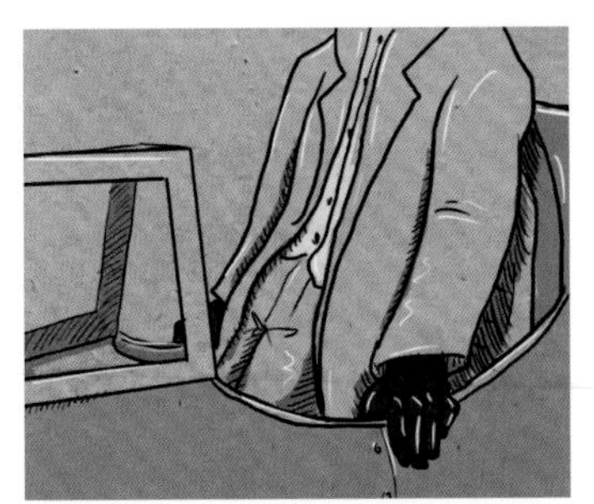

We were into the fight again

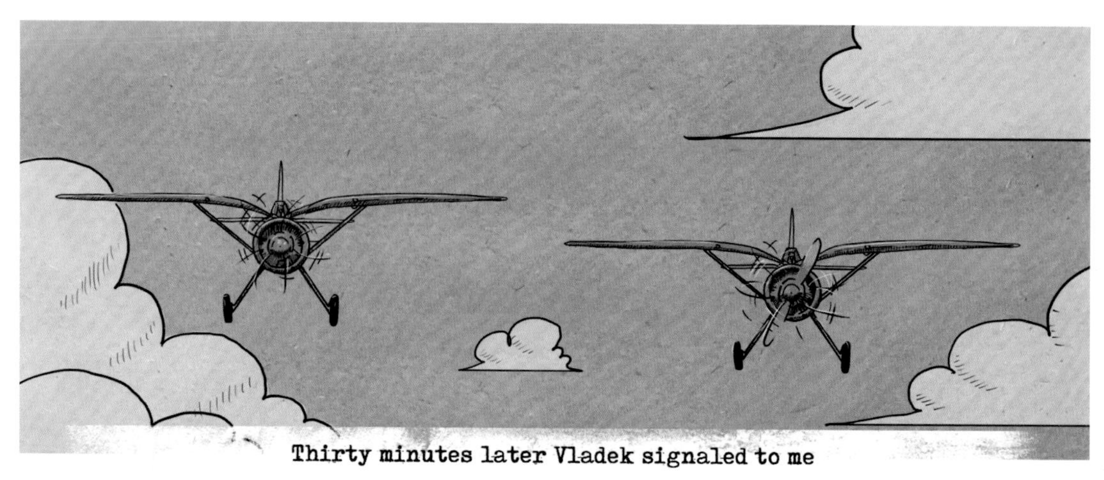
Thirty minutes later Vladek signaled to me

Enemy below

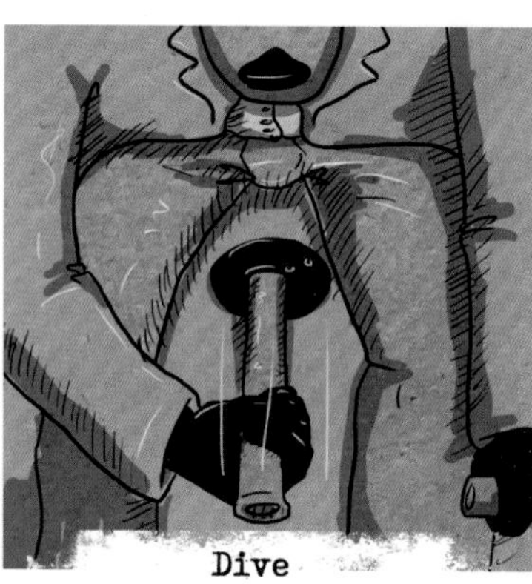
Dive

VARRMMMMMMMMMMMMM
A German Dornier Bomber rumbled in the sky

We moved in

We could catch them in a dive

Vladek first!

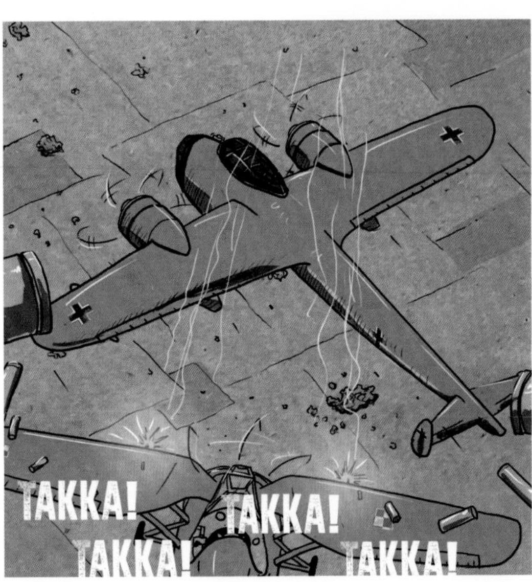
TAKKA!
TAKKA!
TAKKA!
TAKKA!

TING!
TING!
TING!
TING!
TING!
TING!
TING!
TING!

FSSSSSSSS

PLOOM!
SUCCESS!

SHOOT, ZAN!

Perfect timing

As the German crew emerged

I saw that they were boys, and terrified

CLITCHK!

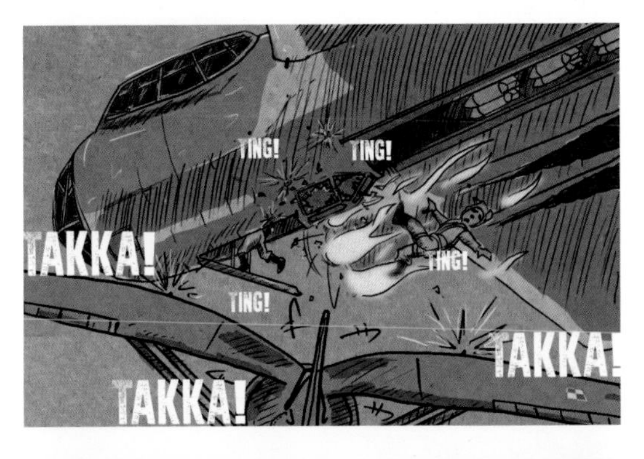
TING!
TING!
TAKKA!
TING!
TING!
TAKKA!
TAKKA!

The death blow worked

WE GOT THEM!
BOOM!

BUT I WILL NEVER FORGET THOSE FACES. I ALWAYS WANTED TO FLY BUT I DID NOT WANT TO KILL...
A realisation came to me

VARRMMMMMMMMM
We returned

VVVRRRRRRRRRRRR

VVVRRRRRRRRRRRR
ONE GERMAN BOMBER LESS!
VVVRRRRRRRRRRRR

WE GOT HIM LESS THAN THREE KILOMETERS FROM HERE

WE'RE MOVING BOYS. GET REFUELED

scratch scratch
FUEL
sigh
BUT WHERE IS GLUPEK TO RECORD OUR KILL?

Glupek was winning the war

Vladek did not like paperwork...

But he did it...

A P.11 from a different squadron came in

Vladek handed in his report

scrunch
scrunch
I saw Glupek's sly hands

VVVRRRRRRRRRRR
But I stayed in my plane

I SAW YOU GUYS GET THAT DORNIER!
CHUG
CHUG
CHUG
The pilot of the new plane called out

YOU WENT IN SO CLOSE, IT WAS FANTASTIC!

I DON'T WANT TO TALK ABOUT IT.

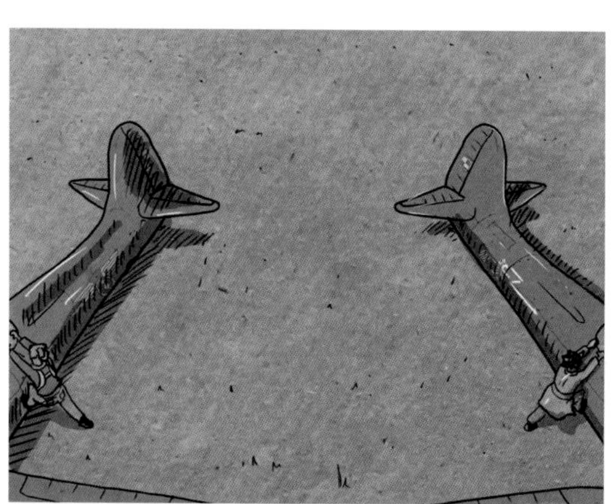

FIRST KILL HUH? I KNOW THE FEELING...

WILL YOU GUYS LET ME REFUEL?
OF COURSE, BUT DON'T ASK GLUPEK. HE'LL TRY TO STOP YOU

THERE ARE SOME WHO THINK THEY WILL WIN THE WAR WITH PAPERWORK. BUT SERIOUSLY, I THINK WE MIGHT BE LOSING THIS ONE

POLAND WILL NEVER BE BEATEN. AND ANYWAY, THE FRENCH AND BRITISH WILL COME

WE'RE TOO FAR AWAY FROM THE BRITS - THEY'LL LET US DOWN FLYBOY

YOU'VE GOT A STRANGE ACCENT, WHERE ARE YOU FROM?

I'VE BEEN LIVING IN AMERICA. IN 1920 MY FATHER FLEW FOR KASZIUSKO SQUADRON SO I THOUGHT I BETTER COME HELP
glug

I'D RATHER BE HOME NOW. MY WIFE AND KIDS ARE IN CHICAGO
Fissss

The American flew into an uncertain sky

Suddenly Glupek was in a rush

The retreating army still had hope when there was no hope.
They fought on

SEPTEMBER 4TH 1939,
10 DOWNING STREET,
LONDON
10
The British cabinet met

WELL GENTLEMEN, WE HAVE DECLARED WAR ON GERMANY. BUT WE NEED A PLAN...
Chamberlain
Churchill
Halifax
Appeasement was Chamberlain's speciality

THE PLAN MUST BE HOW TO ATTACK GERMANY, PRIME MINISTER

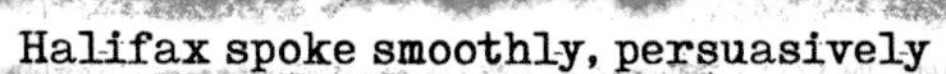
Halifax spoke smoothly, persuasively

IF WE ATTACK THEM THEY WILL ATTACK US, SIR

THE FLEET IS READY.

PERHAPS WE SHOULD WAIT AND SEE IF MR. HITLER WITHDRAWS

Indecision trapped them at the edge of history

IF WE JUST WAIT HITLER WILL OVERRUN POLAND
AND THEN HE WILL CARRY ON

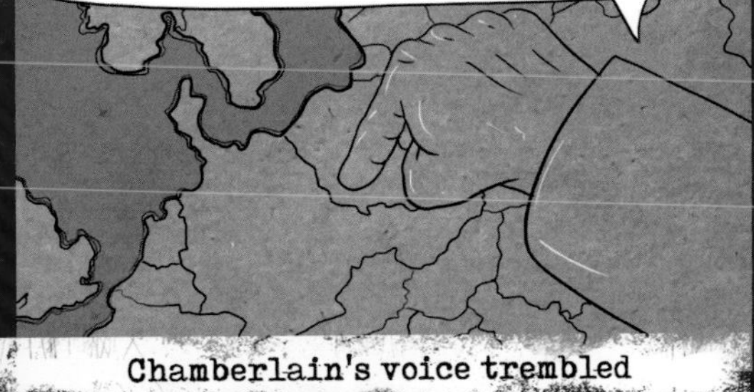
BUT HE IS MOVING EASTWARDS AND MAYBE HE WON'T TURN ON US. MAYBE WE CAN MAKE ANOTHER AGREEMENT LIKE IN MUNICH
Chamberlain's voice trembled

WE COULD DROP SOME LEAFLETS ON GERMANY

SURELY IF WE PUT A GOOD ENOUGH ARGUMENT INTO THE LEAFLETS THE GERMANS WILL SEE THE ERROR IN THEIR WAYS...

BUT POLAND IS SO FAR AWAY...

WE CAN'T REALLY HELP THEM...

AND I DO WISH YOU'D STOP SMOKING INDOORS WINSTON

Poland's fate was sealed

Chamberlain's way of winning the war

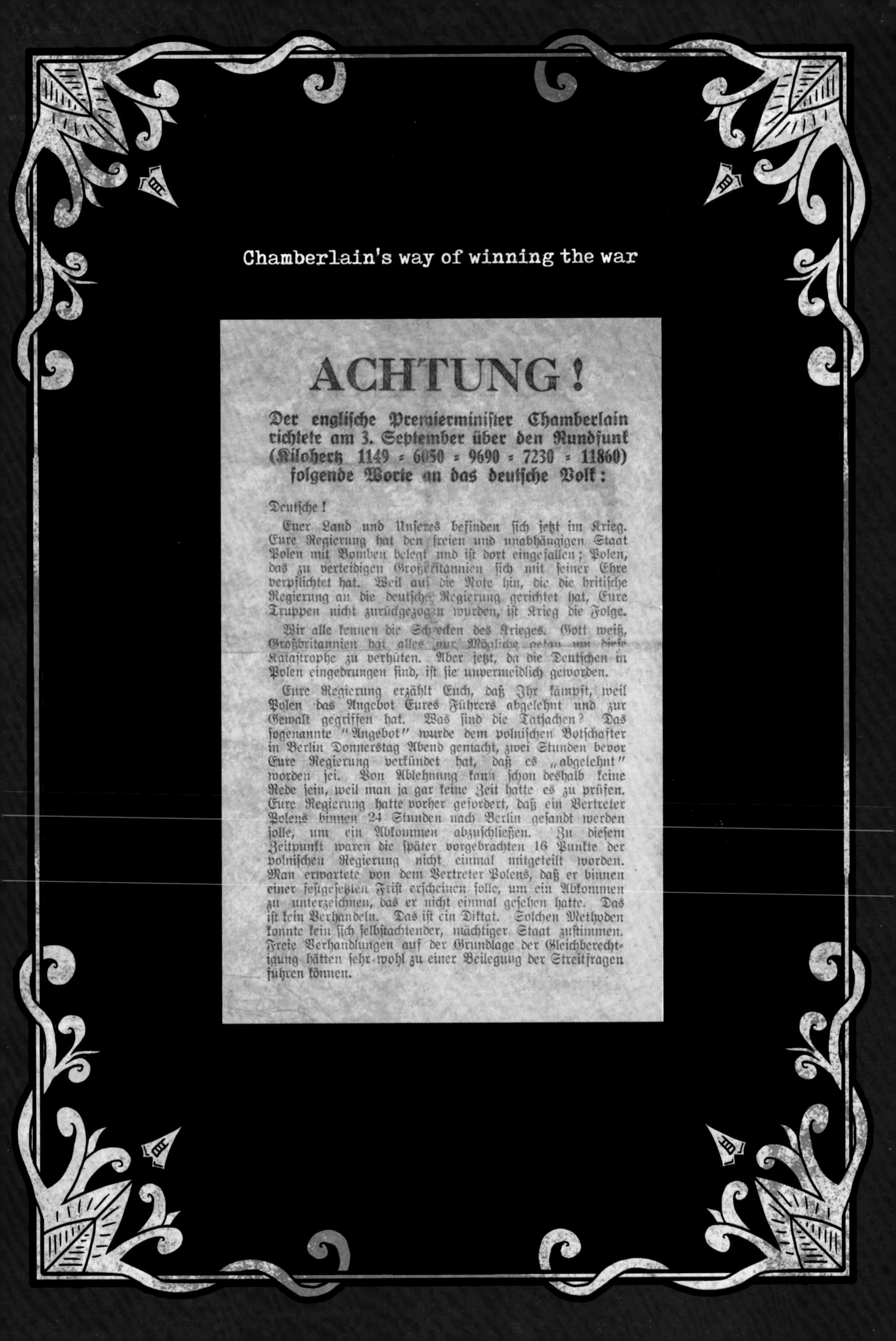

ACHTUNG!

Der englische Premierminister Chamberlain richtete am 3. September über den Rundfunk (Kiloherz 1149 = 6050 = 9690 = 7230 = 11860) folgende Worte an das deutsche Volk:

Deutsche!

Euer Land und Unseres befinden sich jetzt im Krieg. Eure Regierung hat den freien und unabhängigen Staat Polen mit Bomben belegt und ist dort eingefallen; Polen, das zu verteidigen Großbritannien sich mit seiner Ehre verpflichtet hat. Weil auf die Note hin, die die britische Regierung an die deutsche Regierung gerichtet hat, Eure Truppen nicht zurückgezogen wurden, ist Krieg die Folge.

Wir alle kennen die Schrecken des Krieges. Gott weiß, Großbritannien hat alles nur Mögliche getan, um diese Katastrophe zu verhüten. Aber jetzt, da die Deutschen in Polen eingedrungen sind, ist sie unvermeidlich geworden.

Eure Regierung erzählt Euch, daß Ihr kämpft, weil Polen das Angebot Eures Führers abgelehnt und zur Gewalt gegriffen hat. Was sind die Tatsachen? Das sogenannte "Angebot" wurde dem polnischen Botschafter in Berlin Donnerstag Abend gemacht, zwei Stunden bevor Eure Regierung verkündet hat, daß es „abgelehnt" worden sei. Von Ablehnung kann schon deshalb keine Rede sein, weil man ja gar keine Zeit hatte es zu prüfen. Eure Regierung hatte vorher gefordert, daß ein Vertreter Polens binnen 24 Stunden nach Berlin gesandt werden solle, um ein Abkommen abzuschließen. Zu diesem Zeitpunkt waren die später vorgebrachten 16 Punkte der polnischen Regierung nicht einmal mitgeteilt worden. Man erwartete von dem Vertreter Polens, daß er binnen einer festgesetzten Frist erscheinen solle, um ein Abkommen zu unterzeichnen, das er nicht einmal gesehen hatte. Das ist kein Verhandeln. Das ist ein Diktat. Solchen Methoden konnte kein sich selbstachtender, mächtiger Staat zustimmen. Freie Verhandlungen auf der Grundlage der Gleichberechtigung hätten sehr wohl zu einer Beilegung der Streitfragen führen können.

SEPTMEBER 17TH 1939,
ON A NEW AIRFIELD
FAR SOUTH EAST POLAND
The Poles had been retreating before the Germans

WE'RE DOWN TO FLYING ON AUTOMOBILE FUEL. PLANES NEED BETTER FUEL THAN THIS. THIS STUFF HARDLY GETS US IN THE AIR
121 Squadron was down to five planes. Good men had been lost

SIR, WE HAVE BEEN ORDERED TO RETREAT TO ROMANIA

ROMANIA, WHAT? WHY?

HALF OUR FLYERS ARE DEAD
I DO NOT WANT THEM TO HAVE DIED FOR NOTHING!

WE MUST STAY HERE AND KILL MORE GERMANS. WE CAN STILL STOP THEM
GO TO ROMANIA
SMACK

WE ARE NOT BEATEN!
WE WON'T BE BEATEN!

I HAVE NEWS THE RUSSIANS HAVE ATTACKED FROM THE EAST SIR. WE THOUGHT THEY MIGHT BE COMING TO HELP BUT THEY HAVE BEEN FIRING ON OUR TROOPS. WE WERE ATTACKED FROM THE WEST AND NOW WE ARE BETRAYED FROM THE EAST
Disaster

ARE YOU SURE?
WE ARE SURE SIR. THEY ARE COMING TO AVENGE THE 1920 WAR. THEY ARE ON THE SIDE OF THE GERMANS
AND WHERE ARE THE FRENCH? THE BRITISH?

OUR ALLIES HAVE NOT COME. WE HAVE NO NEWS EXCEPT FOR A REPORT THAT THEY DROPPED LEAFLETS ON GERMANY

LEAFLETS! NOT BOMBS!? WHAT KIND OF ALLY IS THAT.

THE MESSAGE SAYS THAT OUR GOVERNMENT AND THE ARMY IS TO FORM OUTSIDE THE MOTHERLAND. WE MUST LEAVE NOW. THE RUSSIANS ARE VERY CLOSE

AND DEFINITELY NO FRENCH, NO BRITISH?
It was hard to believe

NO. NOTHING SIR...

THEN WE MUST GO, I HAVE TO OBEY ORDERS

IF WE ARE DEFEATED IN THIS FIGHT WE MUST SHOW THEM WE ARE NOT DEFEATED IN WAR. A WAR THAT LASTS FOREVER IF IT HAS TO. POLAND WILL LIVE.
My friend Teddy spoke for everyone

LOOK! OUR TRUCKS ARE COMING UP THE ROAD! IF THEY CARRY FUEL MAYBE WE'LL HAVE A CHANCE...

HERE I AM AT LAST!
VVVRRRRRRMMMMMM

The captain was furious

Glupek spoke plaintively

WWWHUUUUMM
FFFF
KKKRRRR
PFFSSSSS

MAYBE THE GERMANS WOULD PAY US IF WE WERE NICE TO THEM AND TOLD THEM EVERYTHING...

WHAT ABOUT OUR WIVES!
OUR FAMILIES!
OUR CHILDREN!
WE CAN'T STOP FIGHTING!

GROUND CREWS GET INTO TRUCKS. MAKE YOUR WAY AS BEST YOU CAN. I DON'T WANT TO LEAVE BUT WE MUST MOVE OUT!

Most of the flyers took their planes across the border, except...

CLITCHK

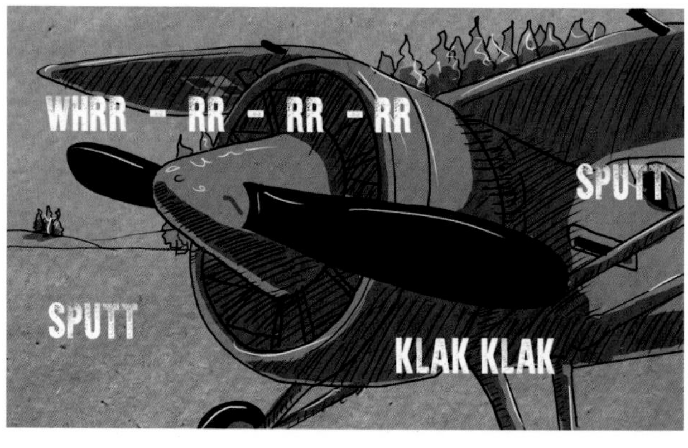
WHRR - RR - RR - RR
SPUTT
SPUTT
KLAK KLAK

Impure fuel caused the planes to be difficult to start

The driver called out

Glupek the hero left me...

Alone

WHRR - RR - RR - RR
SPUTT
KLAK KLAK

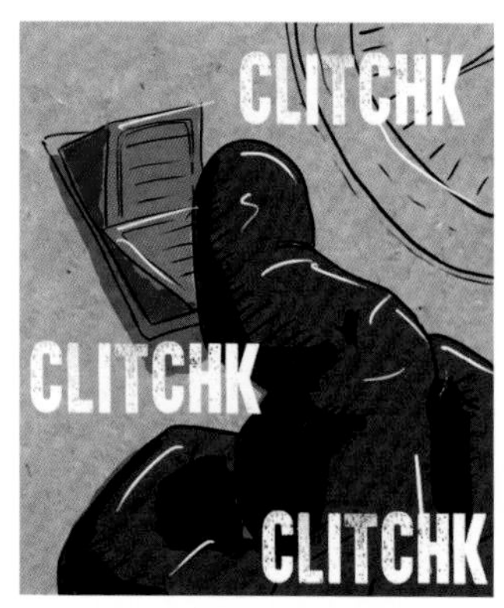
CLITCHK
CLITCHK
CLITCHK

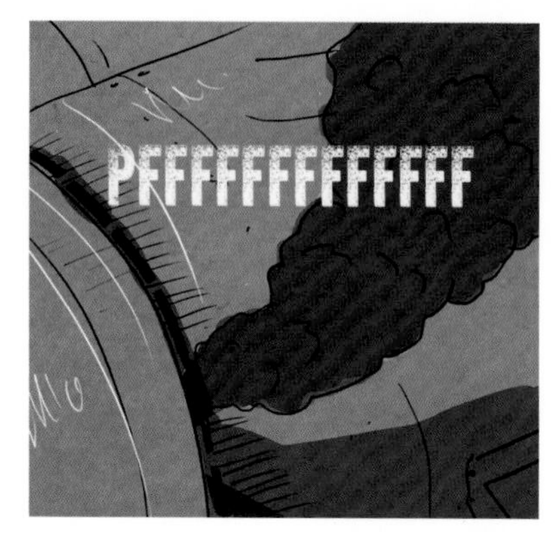
PFFFFFFFFFFFFF

It can be done alone

VVVRRRRRRRRR
The engine roared into life

RRRRRRRRRRRRR
A quick leap and in

ZZZZEEEEOOO...

!WHUMP!

I cleared the trees only to discover Russian troops below

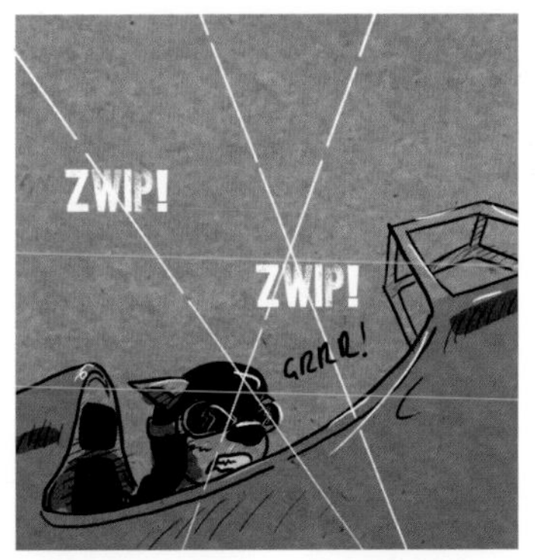

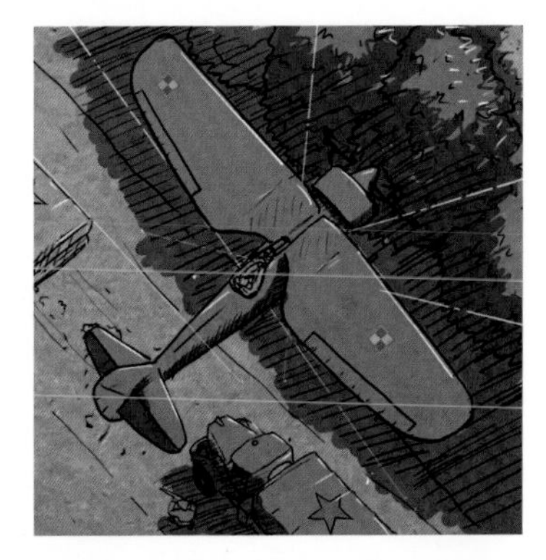

Made it

THE SAME DAY, IN THE WOODS WELL EAST OF GRAJEWO
Walter, my brother, moved cautiously. He had been wandering for days and was hungry
CRUNCH
THANK GOD IT'S YOU WALTER
MY DAD TOLD ME TO HIDE IN THE WOODS
It was Robert, a school friend
MINE TOO
BUT HE'S DEAD
THEY SHOT HIM.
I DON'T KNOW WHAT HAPPENED TO MY DAD.
-
MAYBE WE'LL HAVE TO FIGHT FOR OUR COUNTRY
WE WILL DO WHAT WE MUST ROBERT
MAYBE WE WILL BE HEROES
NOT UNLESS WE FIND SOMETHING TO EAT...
The forest swallowed the voices of the boys

QUIET WE'RE SURROUNDED.
A sudden sense of threat
I THINK YOU WANT TO COME WITH ME, MY BOYS
The leader's voice was filled with sarcasm
AH YES, I KNEW YOUR FATHERS FROM GRAJEWO - WE WILL TAKE CARE OF YOU
THAT'S OLD MAN GRETZIM FROM BIALYSTOCK. - DAD SAYS HE LIVES OFF BRIBES FROM THE TOWN COUNCIL

WE HAVE PHEASANT STEW BACK AT CAMP
WE WILL FEED YOU BOYS...

The partisans were looking for something along the road
WHAT'S GOING ON? THOSE ARE RUSSIAN FLAGS
DON'T WORRY, THEY WILL SURELY BE OUR FRIENDS
A white flag was waved
Then
Gretzim switched flags
I TOLD YOU THESE GUYS WERE COMMUNIST
THEY'RE ALL WE'VE GOT WALTER, STICK WITH THEM

COME CLOSER!

DON'T SHOOT! WE ARE COMMUNIST POLES. WE THINK LIKE YOU THINK. WE ARE FRIENDS
WE HATE OUR GOVERNMENT. WE ARE PROLETERIAT. WE LIKE STALIN

AND YOU ARE OUR FRIENDS TOO, IF THIS IS TRUE.
COME...
The Russian spoke smoothly
COME DRINK VODKA WITH ME...

DRINK VODKA IS BIG SIGN OF RUSSIAN FRIENDSHIP
FRIENDSHIP WITH NICE COMMUNIST FROM POLAND

NOSTROVIA!

DO YOU HAVE GUNS?
His voice was hypnotic

HMMMM, HUNTING GUNS, NOT VERY GOOD
SHOW THEM OUR GUNS MY CHILDREN...

MORE VODKA MY FRIEND!

IT IS NO GOOD YOU AND YOUR BOYS WEAR RAGS. YOU MUST LOOK LIKE SOLDIERS AND WE WILL GIVE YOU PROPER GUNS

WE HAVE SOME NICE UNIFORMS BEHIND THE STOREHOUSE...

HERE, GIVE US YOUR GUNS AND GET YOUR NEW UNIFORMS BEHIND THE SHED
WE'RE ALRIGHT, THANK Y-

COME MY FRIEND, WE WILL HELP YOU

HOW KIND YOU ARE, WE KNEW WE WOULD BE TREATED WELL. COME BOYS...

JUST GO STAND BY THE WALL OVER THERE, WE WILL BRING YOUR NEW UNIFORMS
SEE HOW NICE THESE COMMUNIST PEOPLE ARE WALTER?
COME WITH ME ROBERT! SOMETHING IS WRONG... LET'S RUN
Walter spoke urgently
NOW!
WAL-
CLITCHK!
TAKKA TAKKA
TAKKA TAKKA
TAKKA TAKKA
Be cautious with new friends

"The Germans were not thrown back from Poland. Although lives were lost on both sides, many lives, their armies were victorious. Nobody knew what was going on. Nobody knew what was going to happen next. Confusion and suffering was everywhere.

Then the Russians came from the East. Those who fled before the Germans now had to make up their minds about whether they wanted to be taken by the Russians or whether to try to return to their homes, which the Germans now occupied.

History tells us that Warsaw fought on bravely, and that is true. It was hard to carry on. First the Germans bombed the waterworks so that there was no water. Then they firebombed the city and the fires could not be put out. The city had to surrender.

So Poland was occupied by the Germans and the Russians. The two sides of the country suffered equally.

Himmler, the head of the SS, announced: "All Poles will disappear from the world." All normality vanished."

SEPTEMBER 17TH 1939. THE POLISH ARMY RETREATS

"Many of these who marched did not know that eventually they would be going all the way to Iran, and then onwards to Monte Cassino. But many of those officers who marched would not get as far. They were heading towards a place in the woods called Katyn."

My plane limped across the border into Romania

The other 121 Squadron planes were there. And a few others

It was the American who walked up. Somehow he was everywhere

The Captain always had a plan

His voice was filled with emotion

We felt only defiance

WE WILL FIGHT THE GERMANS TO THE END
WE WILL FIGHT THE RUSSIANS TO THE END

POLAND WILL SURVIVE, IF ONLY IN OUR HEARTS FOR SOME TIME. YOU WILL FIGHT FOR YOUR SWEETHEARTS AND YOUR CHILDREN, AND YOU WILL FIGHT TO THE DEATH IF YOU MUST.

THERE IS NO FUEL FOR THESE PLANES

GET OUT OF HERE
GO BY TRUCK OR BY TRAIN

AND MAYBE WE'LL MEET IN BUCHAREST

GOOD LUCK AND GOD BLESS

The American was good with plans too

The Romanians came forward

A PZL.23 Bomber

The lower gunner position was a squeeze

It was destination Bucharest

The Polish Embassy in Bucharest

The French Embassy was next door

ALL OF YOU, STAND IN A LINE
shoo shoo

COWARDS! OUR FRENCH HEROES WOULD NEVER AV RUN AWAY

MY SON DIED IN LA GUERRE AT VERDUN AND EE WOULD NEVER AV DONE AS YOU AV

I WILL GIVE YOU VISAS AND YOU CAN GO TO DIG LATRINES IN FRANCE BUT YOU MEN WILL NEVER FIGHT
As you know, the worst insult to a dog is to be called a man

GRRRRRR

TAKE THE VISA AND SHUT UP ZAN. WE'LL GET TO THE HARBOUR AND GET OUT OF THIS COUNTRY SOMEHOW

At the port in Constanta, all of us waited surreptitiously for nightfall

A ship anchored at sea had been arranged

INSIDE, QUICKLY

THIS SHIP STINKS!

THEY SAY IT NORMALLY CARRIES DONKEYS TO BAYREUTH. AT LEAST THERE ARE BLANKETS

An uncomfortable sensation

OH NO!

THE SHIP NORMALLY CARRIES A CARGO OF DONKEYS... BUT THE CARGO OF DONKEYS IS...

FLEAS!
SCRATCH SCRATCH
SCRATCH SCRATCH

Photo of Piotr as pilot

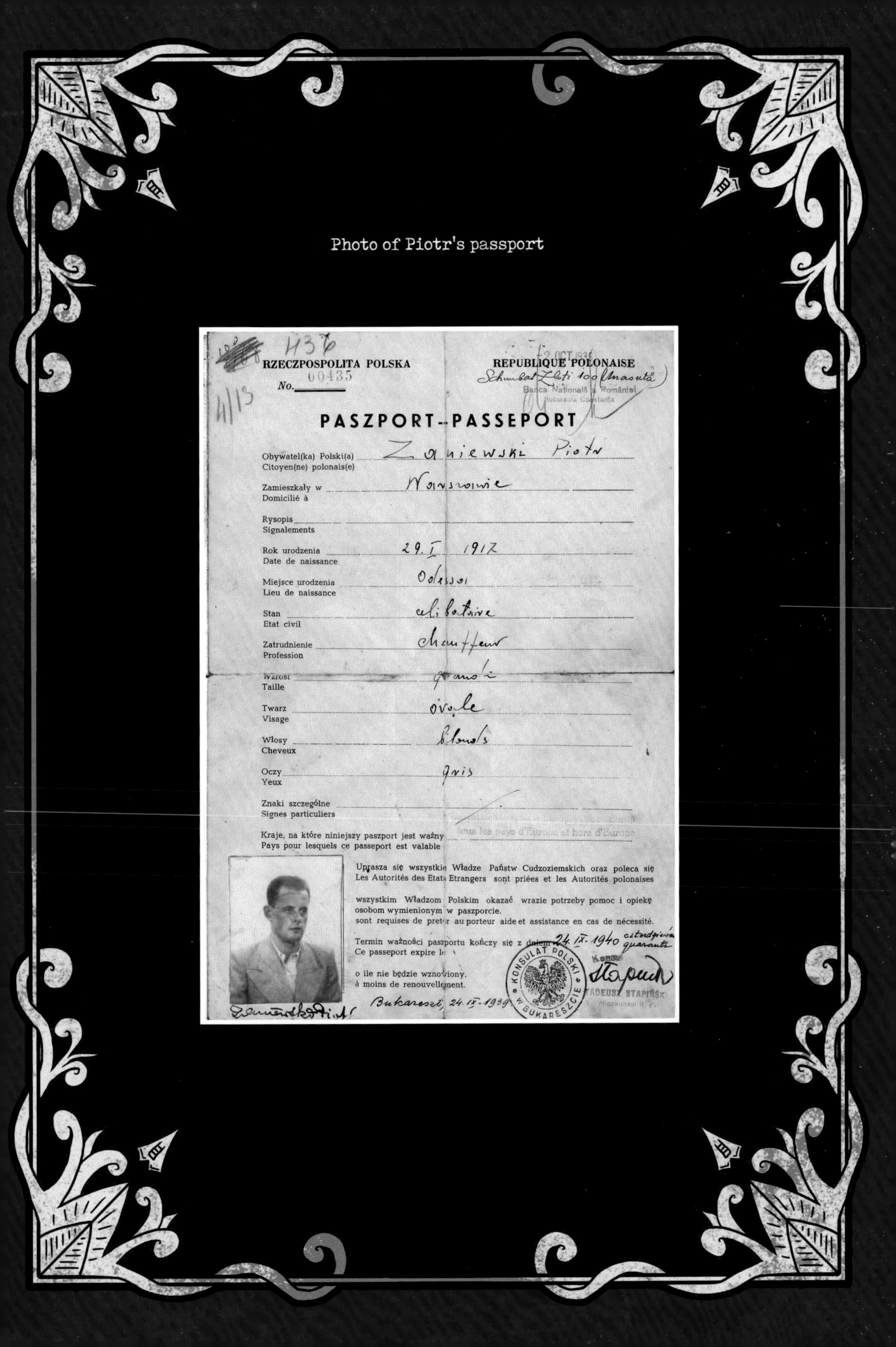

Photo of Piotr's passport

RZECZPOSPOLITA POLSKA

REPUBLIQUE POLONAISE

No. 00435

PASZPORT – PASSEPORT

Obywatel(ka) Polski(a) / Citoyen(ne) polonais(e): Zaniewski Piotr

Zamieszkały w / Domicilié à: Warszawie

Rysopis / Signalements

Rok urodzenia / Date de naissance: 29. I. 1917

Miejsce urodzenia / Lieu de naissance: Odessa

Stan / Etat civil: célibataire

Zatrudnienie / Profession: chauffeur

Wzrost / Taille: grande

Twarz / Visage: ovale

Włosy / Cheveux: blonds

Oczy / Yeux: gris

Znaki szczególne / Signes particuliers

Kraje, na które niniejszy paszport jest ważny / Pays pour lesquels ce passeport est valable: tous les pays d'Europe et hors d'Europe

Uprasza się wszystkie Władze Państw Cudzoziemskich oraz poleca się wszystkim Władzom Polskim okazać wrazie potrzeby pomoc i opiekę osobom wymienionym w paszporcie.

Les Autorités des Etats Etrangers sont priées et les Autorités polonaises sont requises de prêter au porteur aide et assistance en cas de nécessité.

Termin ważności paszportu kończy się z dniem / Ce passeport expire le 24. IX. 1940

o ile nie będzie wznowiony. / à moins de renouvellement.

Bukareszt, 24. IX. 1939

KONSULAT POLSKI W BUKARESZCIE

TADEUSZ STAPIŃSKI

Banca Natională a României

SEPTEMBER 24TH 1939,
AT THE SAME TIME
ON THE ZAN FARM NEAR GRAJEWO
My mother Sophie was alone. My father in the soil
I MUST GO INTO TOWN, I NEED TO KNOW WHAT'S GOING ON...

THE RUSSIANS?
She knew the flag too well

I WONDER WHERE MY BOYS ARE NOW?

HUH!

YOU, STOP!

WHERE ARE YOUR PAPERS?

DON'T SHOOT!

LATE OCTOBER 1939,
OFF THE COAST OF SARDINIA

APPARENTLY THERE ARE ITALIAN SUBMARINES IN THESE WATERS

WUHHH...
In the dark below decks, still itchy and the ship rolling

YOU ARE SEASICK ZAN. ANY MORE OF THIS AND WE'LL BE SAILORS NOT FLYERS

FLYING NEVER MADE ME FEEL THIS SICK...

WE'RE SLOWING DOWN...

LET'S GO TAKE A LOOK
The American just wanted to get up on deck

BLOOP
BLOOP
BLOOP

TSSSSSSSS
Mussolini had not yet entered the war, but it could've happened at any time

MI SCUZI, WHERE YOU THINK YOU A GOING?

TO FRANCE
AND WHAT SHIPPA YOU ARE?
SHIPPA OF FRANCE
NO POLISHA FLYERS?
NO... NO.
YOU GOTTA ANY WINE OR A GIRLS?
I WISH WE DID

THENA WE WON'T A WASTE A TORPEDO ON YOU
NO WAR A YETTA! ARRIVEDERCI!

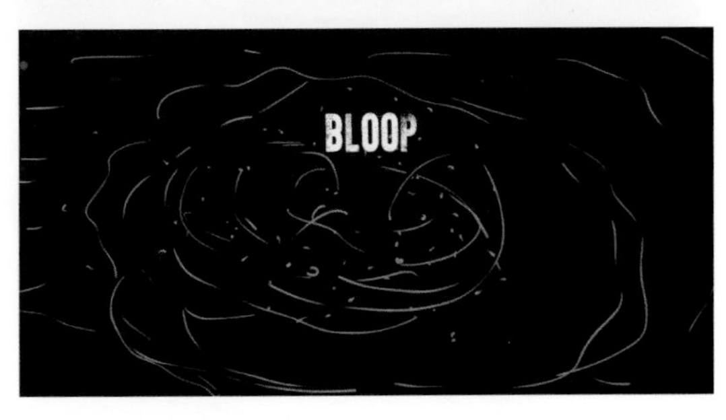
BLOOP

OCTOBER 31ST 1939,
THE PORT OF MARSEILLE
FRANCE
LISTINGS
U.S.S.S
U.S.S.S
DES ESPION
EN EUROPE
We had been posted to different places

WHAT DO ALL THOSE LETTERS BEHIND YOUR NAME STAND FOR, AMERICAN?
LE PORT DE MARSEILLES

DON'T KNOW. THEY MUST HAVE GOT SOMETHING WRONG WITH MY UNIVERSITY DEGREE...

YOU GUYS ARE POSTED TO ISTRES. AND I AM GOING TO, ER, ENGLAND
MARSEILLES
LISTINGS
U.S.S.S.

IT'S BEEN GREAT TO FIGHT WITH YOU AND TO TRAVEL WITH YOU

WE'LL MEET AGAIN.
It was a parting of the ways

WE'LL SEE YOU AGAIN FOR SURE AMERICAN. GOOD LUCK!

ARLY NOVEMBER 1939,
A COOL DAY IN
ISTRES, FANCE
BASE AERIÉNNE

NICE AIRFIELD BUT WHERE ARE ALL THE PLANES?
We were keen to get back into the fight

YOU PILOTS MUST WAIT.

YOU POLES ARE NOT GOOD ENOUGH TO FLY PLANES

YOU LOST YOUR WAR. WHY SHOULD WE LET YOU FLY?

Partisans
NEUTRAL
Arms to Germany
N
E
POLAND
GERMANY &
CONQUESTS
(HITLER)
NEUTRAL
BRITAIN
(CHURCHILL)
many spies
gunmen
GERMANY
Paris
NEUTRAL
SOON TO BE
ATTACKED
FRANCE
Resistance
forming
VICHY
(PETAIN)
ITALY
(IL DUCE)
Zan's current location
Partisans
N
E
U
T
R
A
L
SPAIN
(FRANCO)
many spies
Complicated
VICHY

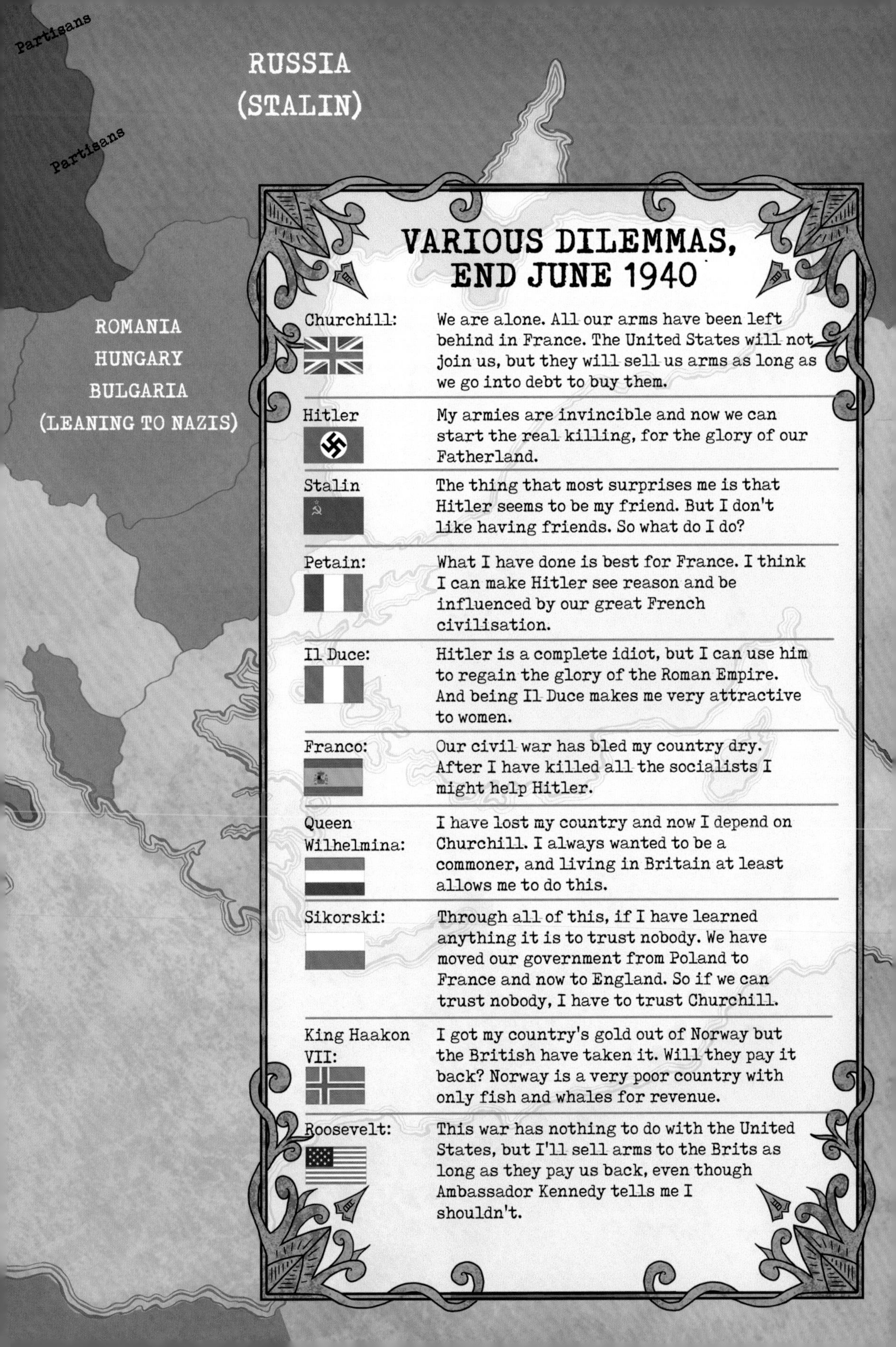

VARIOUS DILEMMAS, END JUNE 1940

Churchill:	We are alone. All our arms have been left behind in France. The United States will not join us, but they will sell us arms as long as we go into debt to buy them.
Hitler	My armies are invincible and now we can start the real killing, for the glory of our Fatherland.
Stalin	The thing that most surprises me is that Hitler seems to be my friend. But I don't like having friends. So what do I do?
Petain:	What I have done is best for France. I think I can make Hitler see reason and be influenced by our great French civilisation.
Il Duce:	Hitler is a complete idiot, but I can use him to regain the glory of the Roman Empire. And being Il Duce makes me very attractive to women.
Franco:	Our civil war has bled my country dry. After I have killed all the socialists I might help Hitler.
Queen Wilhelmina:	I have lost my country and now I depend on Churchill. I always wanted to be a commoner, and living in Britain at least allows me to do this.
Sikorski:	Through all of this, if I have learned anything it is to trust nobody. We have moved our government from Poland to France and now to England. So if we can trust nobody, I have to trust Churchill.
King Haakon VII:	I got my country's gold out of Norway but the British have taken it. Will they pay it back? Norway is a very poor country with only fish and whales for revenue.
Roosevelt:	This war has nothing to do with the United States, but I'll sell arms to the Brits as long as they pay us back, even though Ambassador Kennedy tells me I shouldn't.

NOVEMBER 1939, GERMAN-OCCUPIED POLAND
After the Russians, Walter trusted nobody. He hid in the woods and lived off the land for months, but could not do it anymore. He staggered starving to a sinister group of huts deep in the forest and came across a new group of partisans
ARE YOU A SPY FOR THE FILTHY GERMANS?

OF COURSE NOT!
THEY KILLED MY DAD!

SO WHAT IS IT THAT YOU WANT?..

...

TO FIGHT!

SO YOU WANT TO BE A PARTISAN. WHERE IS YOUR GUN?

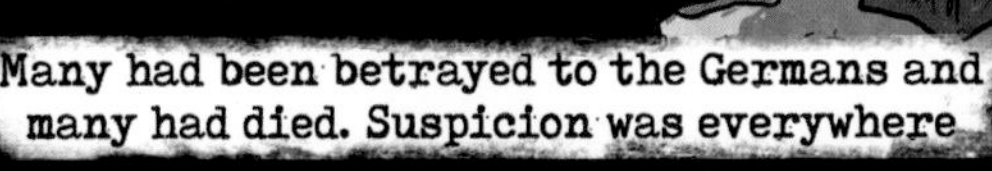
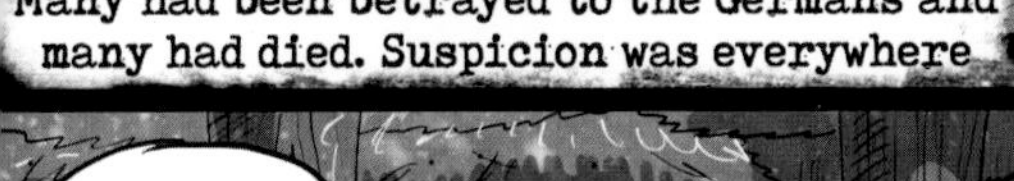
Many had been betrayed to the Germans and many had died. Suspicion was everywhere

I DO NOT HAVE ONE

WELL THEN YOU CANNOT BE A PARTISAN THEN CAN YOU?

THEN HOW DO I GET A GUN?

I DON'T CARE. GET ONE.

HMMFFF!

TRY ASKING THE GERMANS
HAHA
HAHA

I'LL SHOW THEM...
HAHA
HAHA
HAHA

After having walked for most of the day, Walter saw a lone German guard outside a simple church in a small village
MOVE ON POLSKI, MOVE ON!
I NEED TO MAKE A REPORT...
The guard was just a boy like Walter
YOU ANSWERED ME BACK, I CAN ARREST YOU!
HEY, HOW COME YOU SPEAK POLISH?
I COME FROM BRESLAU, MANY OF US SPEAK POLISH THERE. NOW, MOVE!
WE PLAYED FOOTBALL LAST YEAR WITH A TEAM FROM BRESLAU AN-
SMACK!

AARRGGHH!
WHUMP!

HHRRRR!
HHRRRR!

THUMP!
AARGG!

DON'T SHOOT! I DON'T EVEN WANT TO BE HERE, I'LL GO BACK TO MY MOTHER

BANG!
FFFTTTT

His mother would weep in a continent

THUNK!
SO!
Back at the partisan lair

I AM PARTISAN NOW.

NO. MAYBE YOU **ARE** A SPY TO HAVE A WEAPON LIKE THIS. HOLD HIM!

THUMP!

YOU SAID GET A GUN. I GOT ONE. I KILLED A GERMAN TO GET IT. IS THAT NOT ENOUGH?! HOW MANY GERMANS HAVE YOU KILLED?

WAIT. YOU KILLED A GERMAN? WHERE?

OVER NEAR RUPIN. IT'S FAR FROM HERE...
YOU FOOL!
The partisan leader's voice was filled with dread

BOYS

LET'S GO...

Walter's hands were tied. He and the partisan group went back to the village near Rupin. Ominous smoke was rising

I BELIEVE YOU ARE NOT A SPY BOY...

WHAT HAPPENED!?

THERE'S A WORD FOR IT...

REPRISALS.

FOR EVERY ONE OF THEM THEY KILL FIFTY OF US
SNIIICK!

BUT...

YOU ARE PARTISAN NOW
A complex badge of courage was handed to him

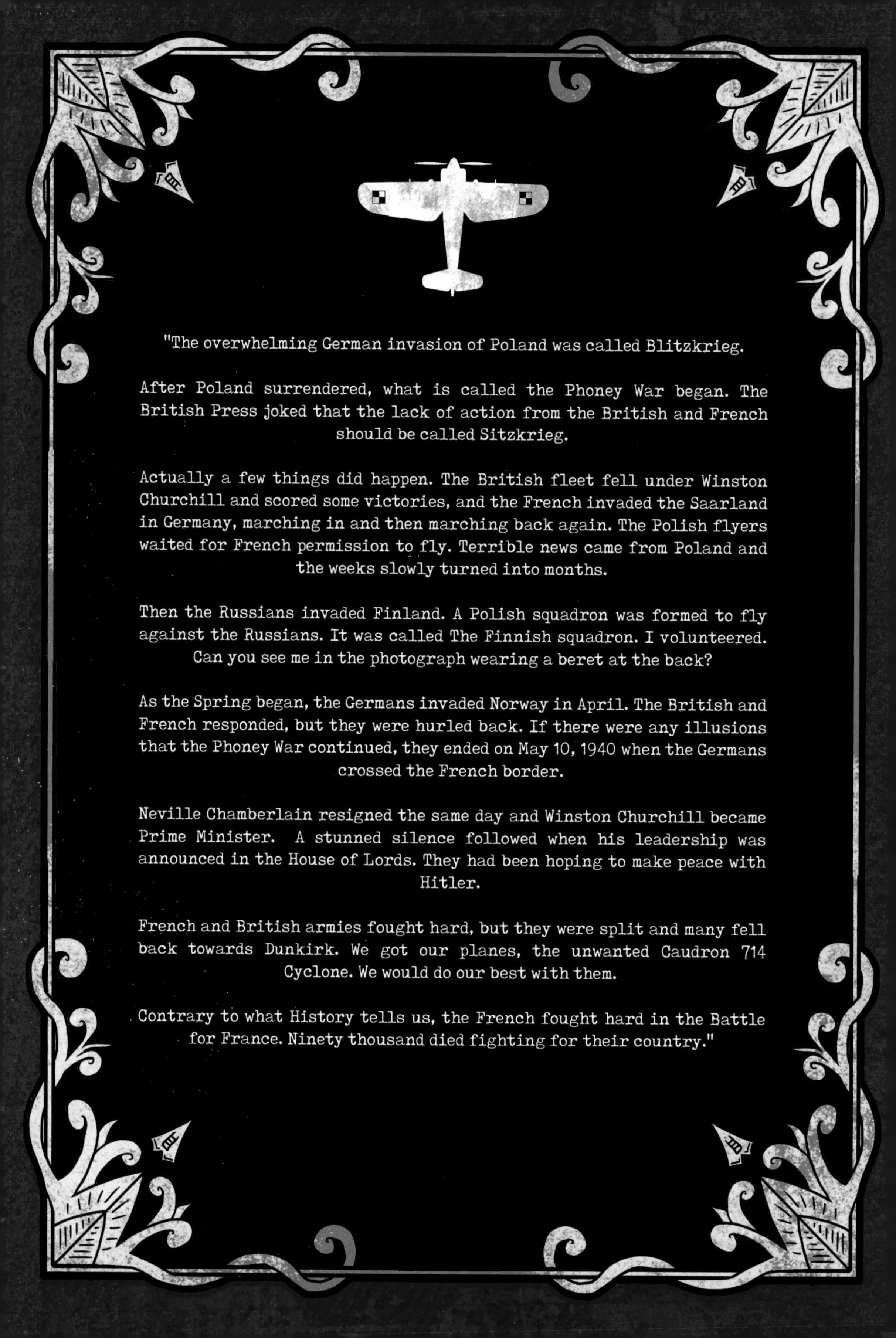

"The overwhelming German invasion of Poland was called Blitzkrieg.

After Poland surrendered, what is called the Phoney War began. The British Press joked that the lack of action from the British and French should be called Sitzkrieg.

Actually a few things did happen. The British fleet fell under Winston Churchill and scored some victories, and the French invaded the Saarland in Germany, marching in and then marching back again. The Polish flyers waited for French permission to fly. Terrible news came from Poland and the weeks slowly turned into months.

Then the Russians invaded Finland. A Polish squadron was formed to fly against the Russians. It was called The Finnish squadron. I volunteered. Can you see me in the photograph wearing a beret at the back?

As the Spring began, the Germans invaded Norway in April. The British and French responded, but they were hurled back. If there were any illusions that the Phoney War continued, they ended on May 10, 1940 when the Germans crossed the French border.

Neville Chamberlain resigned the same day and Winston Churchill became Prime Minister. A stunned silence followed when his leadership was announced in the House of Lords. They had been hoping to make peace with Hitler.

French and British armies fought hard, but they were split and many fell back towards Dunkirk. We got our planes, the unwanted Caudron 714 Cyclone. We would do our best with them.

Contrary to what History tells us, the French fought hard in the Battle for France. Ninety thousand died fighting for their country."

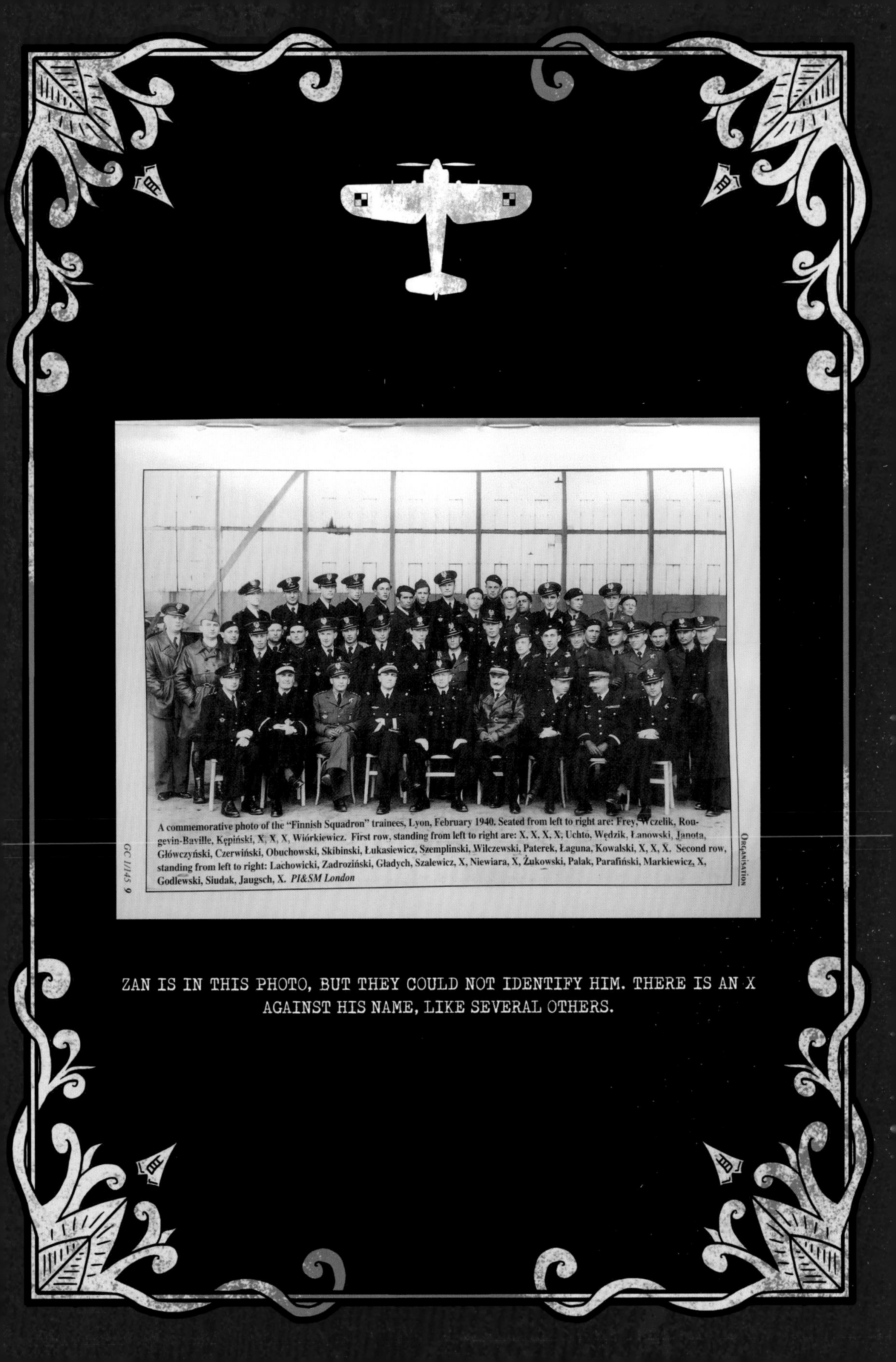
GC I/I45 9
A commemorative photo of the "Finnish Squadron" trainees, Lyon, February 1940. Seated from left to right are: Frey, Wczelik, Rougevin-Baville, Kępiński, X, X, X, Wiórkiewicz. First row, standing from left to right are: X, X, X, X, Uchto, Wędzik, Łanowski, Janota, Główczyński, Czerwiński, Obuchowski, Skibinski, Łukasiewicz, Szemplinski, Wilczewski, Paterek, Łaguna, Kowalski, X, X, X. Second row, standing from left to right: Lachowicki, Zadroziński, Gładych, Szalewicz, X, Niewiara, X, Żukowski, Palak, Parafiński, Markiewicz, X, Godlewski, Siudak, Jaugsch, X. PI&SM London
ORGANISATION
ZAN IS IN THIS PHOTO, BUT THEY COULD NOT IDENTIFY HIM. THERE IS AN X AGAINST HIS NAME, LIKE SEVERAL OTHERS.

LATE MAY 1940,
ISTRES, FRANCE
THOSE ARE CAUDRON C714'S
For all this time the Poles had no planes to fly

ZE FILTHY BOCHE INVADED US TWO WEEKS AGO AND NOW WE WILL ALLOW YOU TO FLY FOR GLORY

NOT FOR ZE GLORY OF YOUR OWN COUNTRY WHICH SURRENDERED SO EASILY BUT ZE GLORY OF LA FRANCE

ANYWAY... THESE PLANES ARE NOTORIOUS, THE FRENCH CALL THEM "THE FLYING COFFIN" BECAUSE THEY FLY SO BADLY

LOOK! THEY HAVE GLASS ALL OVER THE COCKPIT. MAYBE THEY AREN'T SO BAD...

LET'S TRY THEM OUT!

NOT SO FAST. OFFICERS FIRST.

Our great captain climbed in

WOOOOSH

ZZZEEEEOOOOWWWWWWWW
WOAH!
THEY'RE FAST!

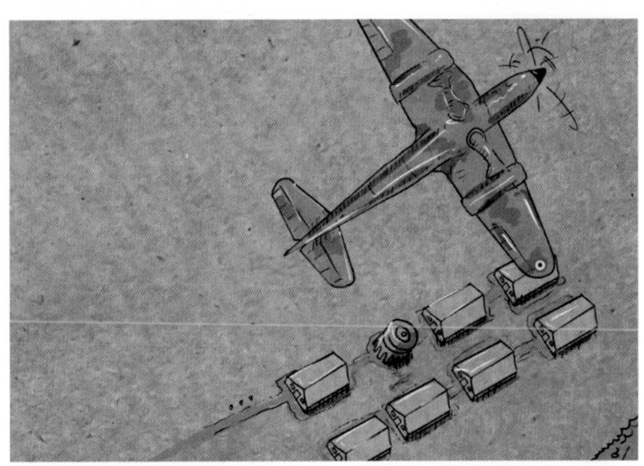

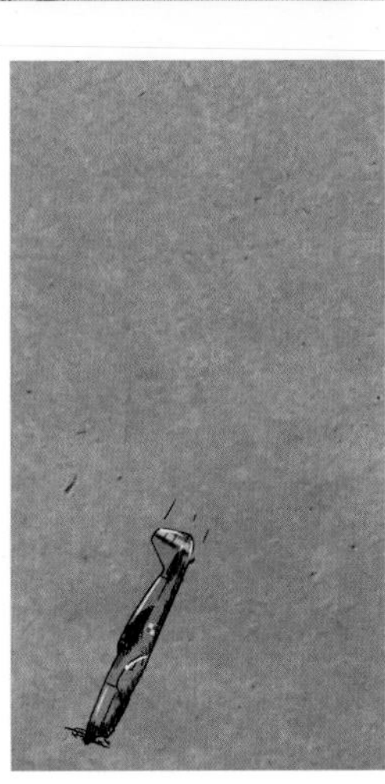

During the war flying accidents killed as many as were killed in combat

Over the course of three weeks

click-click
We pilots learned to fly our new planes

We trained hard every day

Even having mock battles

Then we heard that the Caudron was to be withdrawn from service but
we ignored the order and continued to fly the French plane

ZZZZEEEEOOOOOOWWWW
And at last, we were ready

8th of June. Above the little

town of Vernon, France

We came at them from out of the sun
DAKKA
DAKKA
DAKKA
DAKKA
DAKKA

KKRRRSSSHHH

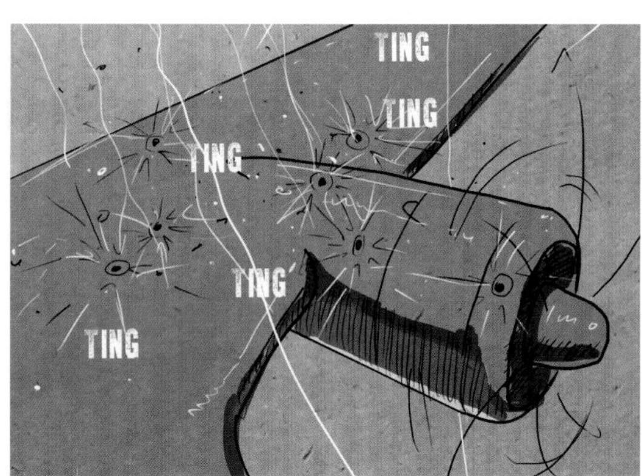
TING
TING
TING
TING
TING

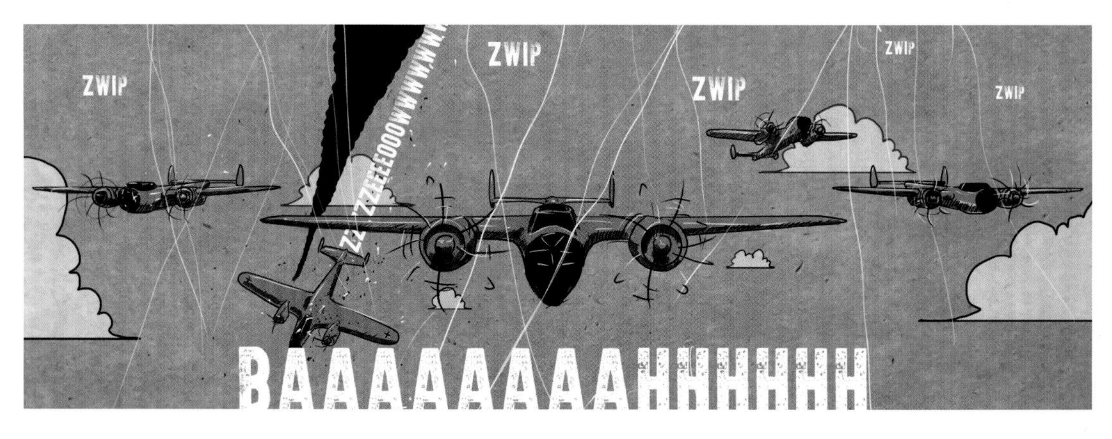
ZWIP
ZWIP
ZWIP
ZWIP
ZWIP
BAAAAAAAHHHHHH

ZZZEEEOOO
WWAAAAHHHHHH
ZZZEEEOOOW
WWOOOSSHH

DAKKDAKKADAKKADAKKA

BATOOMBATOOMBATOOM

KRAK

BOOM

GOT THEM.

LET'S GET BACK TO BASE
VVRRRRRRRRRRRRRRRRR

SLAP

NICE WORK BOYS

WE GOT SIX OF THEM BUT FOUR MORE OF US ARE LOST.

AHEM! EXCUSE ME GENTLEMEN, COME INSIDE S'IL VOUZ PLAIT

INTO ZIS ROOM...

SLAM

HEY! WHAT ARE YOU DOING?!
MESSIEURS, I AM ORDERED TO ARREST YOU BECAUSE WE HAVE SURRENDERED AND WE ARE SUPPOSED TO 'AND YOU TO ZE GERMANS. BUT MESSIEURS, LOOK UP. LOOK UP...

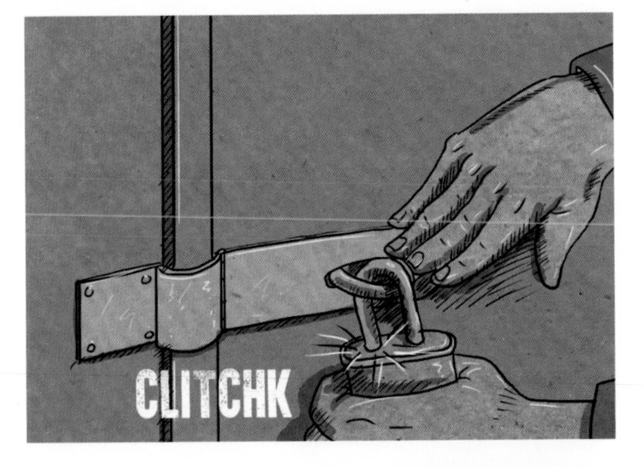
CLITCHK

SO THEY LOCK US UP FOR FIGHTING FOR THEM!
DOOF!
DOOF!
ARE WE BEING GUARDED?

NO I CAN'T HEAR ANYTHING

GOOD, HE TOLD US TO LOOK UP, THERE'S A HATCH...

THEY'RE COMING. GO THE OTHER WAY, MOVE!

IT'S CLEAR
GOOD. LET'S RUN!

FFT
FFT
FFT
FFT

FFT
FFT
FFT
FFT
FFT
FFT
FFT

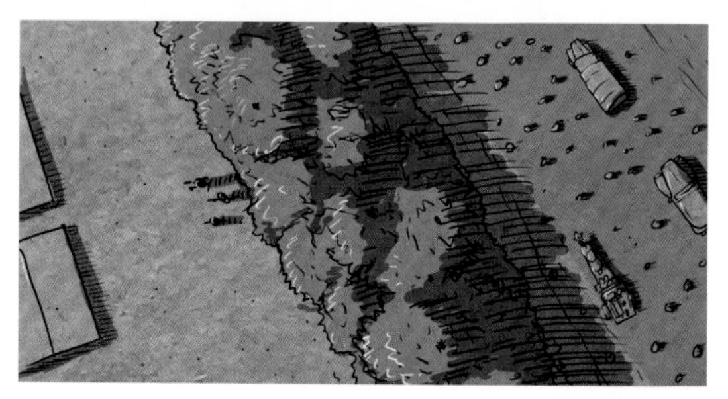

THE ROAD IS FULL OF PEOPLE. BLEND IN

THAT FRENCHMAN WANTED US TO ESCAPE

IS THAT A PLANE UP THERE?

HEY! THIS IS A POLISH MILITARY TRUCK

HEY! POLSKI! POLSKI!
TAP
TAP

CZEŚĆ
WE'RE WITH THE AIRFORCE
CAN WE GET A RIDE?
SURE. I'M HEADED FOR THE PORT IN ST. NAZAIRE, I'M GOING TO TRY CATCH A SHIP

BOOM

DAMMIT! IT'S A STUKA, GET IN! QUICKLY!
ZZEEEEOOOOWWW

THEY'RE HERE TO AVENGE THE PLANES WE SHOT DOWN!
DRIVE!

beep! beep!
ZOOOOM

JUNE 17TH 1940,
APPROACHING THE FRENCH
PORT OF ST. NAZAIRE
ALMOST THERE

SSSKKKKKRRRRTT

KKRRRCCH

WOAH...

I WAS ABOUT TO DELIVER ONE OF MY MOST IMPORTANT SPEECHES OF THE WAR IN THE HOUSE OF COMMONS. EVENTS IN FRANCE HAD TAKEN A DISASTROUS TURN, ALTHOUGH WE HAD SUCCESSFULLY RESCUED A MAJOR PORTION OF OUR ARMY FROM DUNKIRK.
THE REMAINDER OF OUR ARMIES TOGETHER WITH ELEMENTS OF OUR RETREATING ALLIES WERE BEING RESCUED FROM THE WESTERN PORTS OF FRANCE. IN THESE CIRCUMSTANCES, HOW COULD I TELL THE PEOPLE OF BRITAIN OF THE LOSS OF THE LANCASTRIA ON THE 17TH OF JUNE.
THOSE WHO LISTENED TO MY SPEECH NEEDED ENCOURAGEMENT AND TO BE STIFFENED IN THEIR RESOLVE. MANY DIFFICULT DECISIONS HAD TO BE MADE.
THE LOSS OF THE LANCASTRIA WAS BRITAIN'S GREATEST SEA DISASTER.
SIX THOUSAND LIVES WERE LOST, FOUR TIMES AS MANY AS ON THE TITANIC. MANY REPORTS WERE SUPRESSED AND SUBJECT TO A ONE HUNDRED YEAR SECRECY BAN.

After Dunkirk, thousands were evacuated

from French ports in Operation Ariel

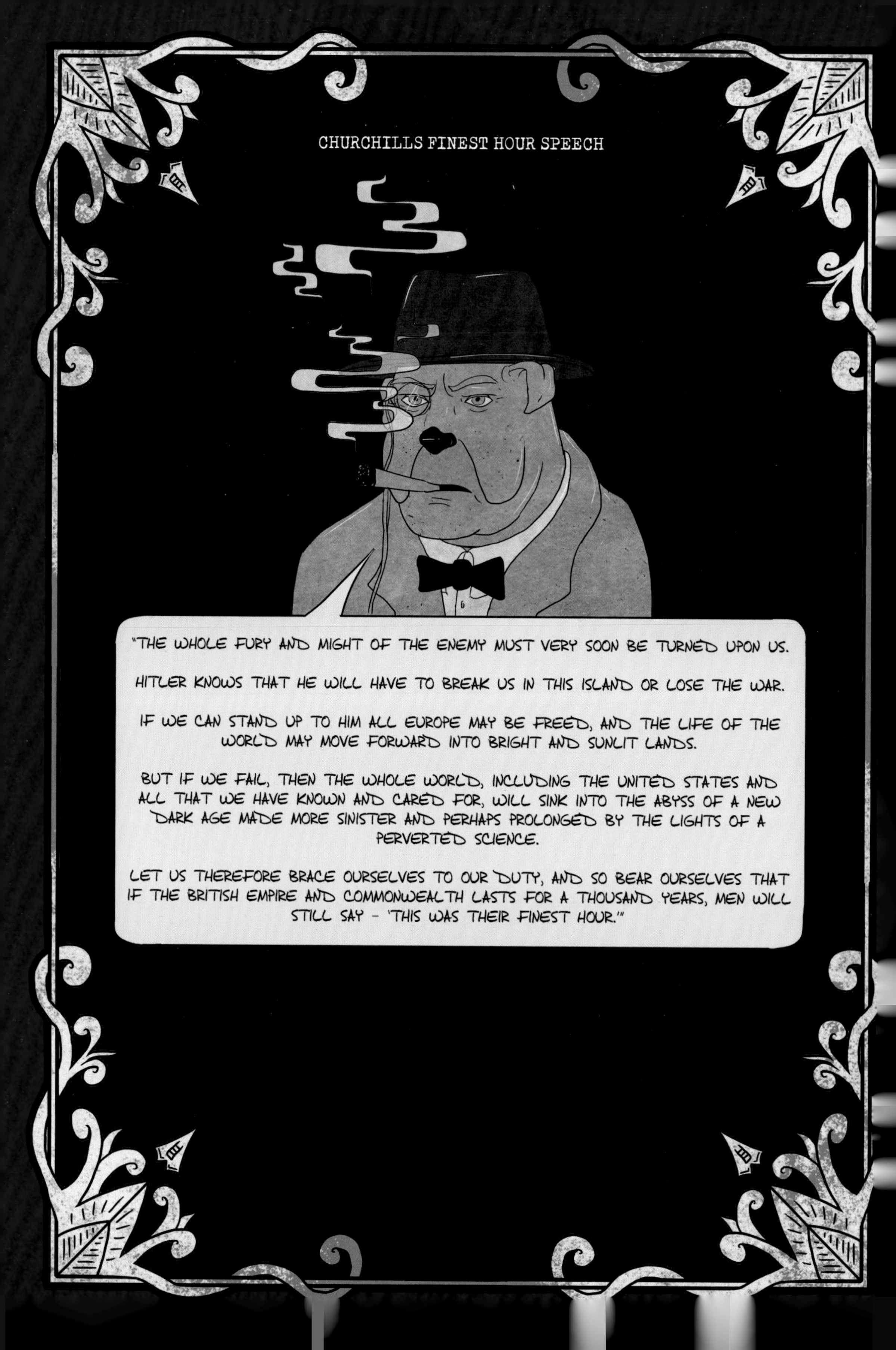
CHURCHILLS FINEST HOUR SPEECH
"THE WHOLE FURY AND MIGHT OF THE ENEMY MUST VERY SOON BE TURNED UPON US.
HITLER KNOWS THAT HE WILL HAVE TO BREAK US IN THIS ISLAND OR LOSE THE WAR.
IF WE CAN STAND UP TO HIM ALL EUROPE MAY BE FREED, AND THE LIFE OF THE WORLD MAY MOVE FORWARD INTO BRIGHT AND SUNLIT LANDS.
BUT IF WE FAIL, THEN THE WHOLE WORLD, INCLUDING THE UNITED STATES AND ALL THAT WE HAVE KNOWN AND CARED FOR, WILL SINK INTO THE ABYSS OF A NEW DARK AGE MADE MORE SINISTER AND PERHAPS PROLONGED BY THE LIGHTS OF A PERVERTED SCIENCE.
LET US THEREFORE BRACE OURSELVES TO OUR DUTY, AND SO BEAR OURSELVES THAT IF THE BRITISH EMPIRE AND COMMONWEALTH LASTS FOR A THOUSAND YEARS, MEN WILL STILL SAY - 'THIS WAS THEIR FINEST HOUR.'"

I SAID GO AWAY! YOU WILL NOT GET ON!

ZAN! COME LOOK!
Then Teddy called

THERE'S ENOUGH FUEL IN THESE ABANDONED TRUCKS TO GET TO THE SOUTH OF FRANCE!

IT'S FIVE HUNDRED KILOMETRES FROM HERE BUT WE'LL GET AWAY FROM THE CROWDS AND SURELY CATCH A SHIP TO THE ISLAND OF GIBRALTAR

GIBRALTAR IS NOT AN ISLAND VLADEK, IT'S A ROCK...
HOW DO YOU KNOW THAT?

I WAS A GEOGRAPHY TEACHER BEFORE THE WAR BEGAN
Tink!

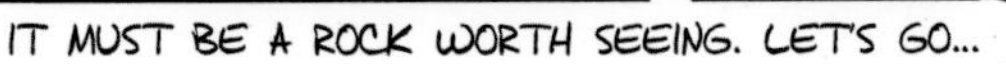
IT MUST BE A ROCK WORTH SEEING. LET'S GO...

VROOOOM

Five hundred kilometers later...
IT'S NO GOOD

THIS PORT IS CROWDED TOO...

I HAVE AN IDEA. A SHORT WAY BACK UP THE ROAD THERE WAS A SIGN FOR AN AIR BASE... MAYBE WE'LL BE LUCKY

VVVVRRRRMMMMMM

BASE AERIENNE
We found the airfield...

NOW THAT'S MY KIND OF BOAT!

Three abandoned Curtis P-36s sat on the empty airfield, bought by the French and hardly used

VVAAAARRRRRRRRRMMMMM

FUEL IS GETTING LOW...
Two hours later

I CAN SEE LAND! THAT MUST BE AFRICA!

20
40
60
FUEL

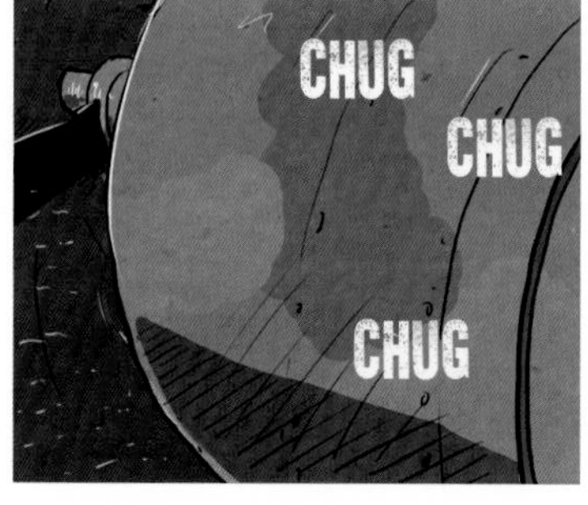
CHUG
CHUG
CHUG

WE'LL GLIDE IN. GENTLEMEN, PRAY FOR FLAT GROUND...

WWHHSSH HHHHHHHH

LAND BY THE TRAIN!

CHOO CHOO

WHAM

KKRRRSSSHHHHHHHHH

CHOOKA CHOOKA
CHOOKA CHOOKA
FFFSSSSSSSS

ARRGGHH LET'S GET OUT
EVERYONE OK?

THIS TRAIN MAY BE HEADED FOR CASABLANCA...
SO WHAT?

SO RUN!

A trainload of many nations.

Defeated but united in a common cause

WOAH...
Casablanca, Morocco

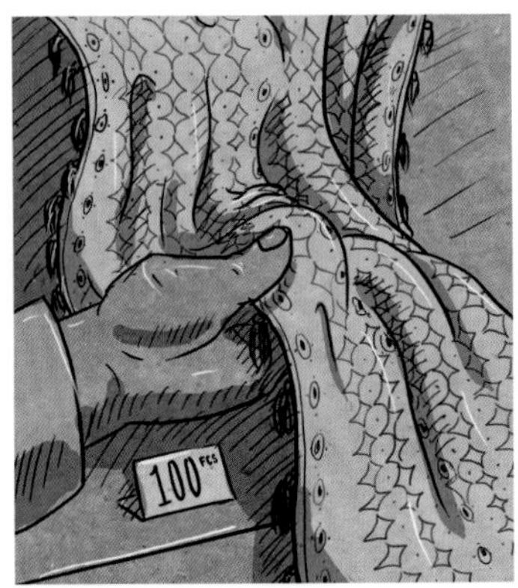
100 FES

THIS PLACE IS AMAZING

Rick's
Café Américain
LET'S GET A DRINK HERE...

WELCOME TO RICK'S!
GLUPEK!?!

WHAT THE HELL ARE YOU DOING HERE!?

WELL THE WAR IS, ERR, OVER. AND A MAN HAS TO MAKE A LIVING. I HAVE AN IMPORTANT JOB IN THE CLUB

MR. GLUPEK...

IF THESE ARE FRIENDS OF YOURS, YOU SHOULD GO WITH THEM, YA KNOW
GET OUTTA THE FREE ZONE. IT AIN'T GONNA LAST MUCH LONGER ANYHOW...

BUT WHY MR. RICK?

MAITRE'D
LISTEN, TAKE THE HINT. YOU COULD SAY YOU'RE FIRED, SONNY. AND BY THE LOOKS OF YOUR FRIENDS HERE, BLACK AND WHITE AIN'T YOUR PROPER UNIFORM

YOU HAD BETTER COME WITH US GLUPEK. YOU CAN TELL US OF ALL YOUR **BRAVE** ADVENTURES. THIS PLACE IS TOO EXPENSIVE FOR US ANYWAY...

THERE IS SOME KIND OF MEETING DOWN AT THE TOWN HARBOUR. COME ON

HEY SAM, PLAY THE PIANNER, AND WE BETTER ADVERTISE FOR A NEW MAITRE'D
RICK, I NEED TO TALK TO YOU...

2012,
ACK ON THE BEACH IN AFRICA
THEY HAD BEEN TALKING ALL DAY
WAIT A MINUTE. YOU'RE TELLING ME A STORY ABOUT THE CASABLANCA MOVIE. THIS IS NOT YOUR STORY.
Café
A son speaks to his father

WELL, IT'S ALMOST TRUE. AND I'M GETTING TIRED
AND THERE WERE SEVERAL PLACES LIKE RICK'S CAFE IN CASABLANCA. WE WENT TO ALL OF THEM AND THAT AMERICAN KEPT FOLLOWING US. ONLY LATER WOULD I FIND OUT WHY...

IF YOU'RE TIRED WE''LL START AGAIN TOMORROW
NO. I'LL CARRY ON.
NONE OF THOSE GIRLS WERE AS BEAUTIFUL AS YOUR MOTHER YOU KNOW, NOT EVEN INGRID BERGMAN IN THAT MOVIE YOU'RE COMPLAINING ABOUT...
Again they look out across the sea,
and again they go back in time

A senior officer spoke to the gathered flyers and soldiers

One ship would turn South for Buenos Aires,
the other went to Gibraltar and then onwards

HEY HAS ANYONE SEEN GLUPEK?
I still had no sealegs

WATCH OUT!

POOOOOT
POOOOOOOT
HOOD
SPLOSH
SPLASH

THAT'S A BRITISH BATTLESHIP

WHERE DO YOU THINK IT'S GOING?

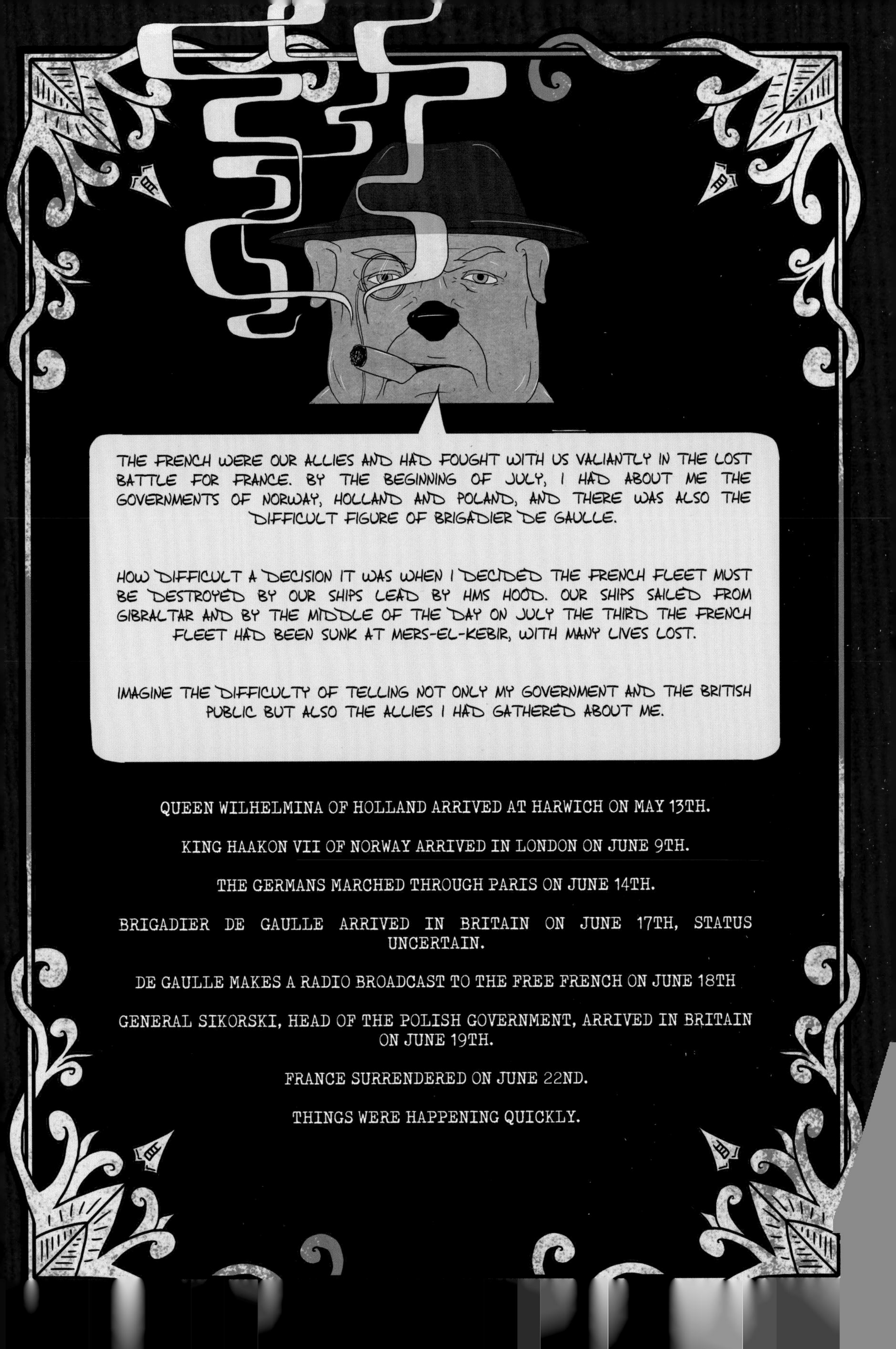
THE FRENCH WERE OUR ALLIES AND HAD FOUGHT WITH US VALIANTLY IN THE LOST BATTLE FOR FRANCE. BY THE BEGINNING OF JULY, I HAD ABOUT ME THE GOVERNMENTS OF NORWAY, HOLLAND AND POLAND, AND THERE WAS ALSO THE DIFFICULT FIGURE OF BRIGADIER DE GAULLE.
HOW DIFFICULT A DECISION IT WAS WHEN I DECIDED THE FRENCH FLEET MUST BE DESTROYED BY OUR SHIPS LEAD BY HMS HOOD. OUR SHIPS SAILED FROM GIBRALTAR AND BY THE MIDDLE OF THE DAY ON JULY THE THIRD THE FRENCH FLEET HAD BEEN SUNK AT MERS-EL-KEBIR, WITH MANY LIVES LOST.
IMAGINE THE DIFFICULTY OF TELLING NOT ONLY MY GOVERNMENT AND THE BRITISH PUBLIC BUT ALSO THE ALLIES I HAD GATHERED ABOUT ME.
QUEEN WILHELMINA OF HOLLAND ARRIVED AT HARWICH ON MAY 13TH.
KING HAAKON VII OF NORWAY ARRIVED IN LONDON ON JUNE 9TH.
THE GERMANS MARCHED THROUGH PARIS ON JUNE 14TH.
BRIGADIER DE GAULLE ARRIVED IN BRITAIN ON JUNE 17TH, STATUS UNCERTAIN.
DE GAULLE MAKES A RADIO BROADCAST TO THE FREE FRENCH ON JUNE 18TH
GENERAL SIKORSKI, HEAD OF THE POLISH GOVERNMENT, ARRIVED IN BRITAIN ON JUNE 19TH.
FRANCE SURRENDERED ON JUNE 22ND.
THINGS WERE HAPPENING QUICKLY.

Cape Finisterre
A Coruna
Lisbon
PORTUGAL
Many Spies
Casablanca
Gibraltar
SPAIN
Bilbao
Prime meridian
3rd July
HMS Hood
attack French
Fleet
Madrid
Guerillas
&
Bandits
French Fleet
Barcelona
Oran
The Flight To Africa
MOROCCO
MAJORCA
MINORCA
N
1940 FRANCE
INVASION &
ESCAPE
SARDINIA
Italian Submarine

IRELAND
Brest
17th June
Sinking of
SS Lancastria
St Nazaire
19th June
Forgotten battle
by cadets
LAST
HOPE
ISLAND
London
Little
Ships
La Rochelle
Bordeaux
Saumur
Route of
truck journey
26th May - 4th June
Evacuation
Dunkirk
Refugees
Paris
10th June
Paris falls
Toulouse
Perpignan
17th June
General Petain calls for surrender
18th June
De Gaulle's defiant broadcast from Britain
Istres
Vichy
10th May
Germany attacks
France
Maginot
Line
Lyons
Marseilles
FRANCE
10th June
Italy attacks France
CORSICA
GERMANY
ITALY

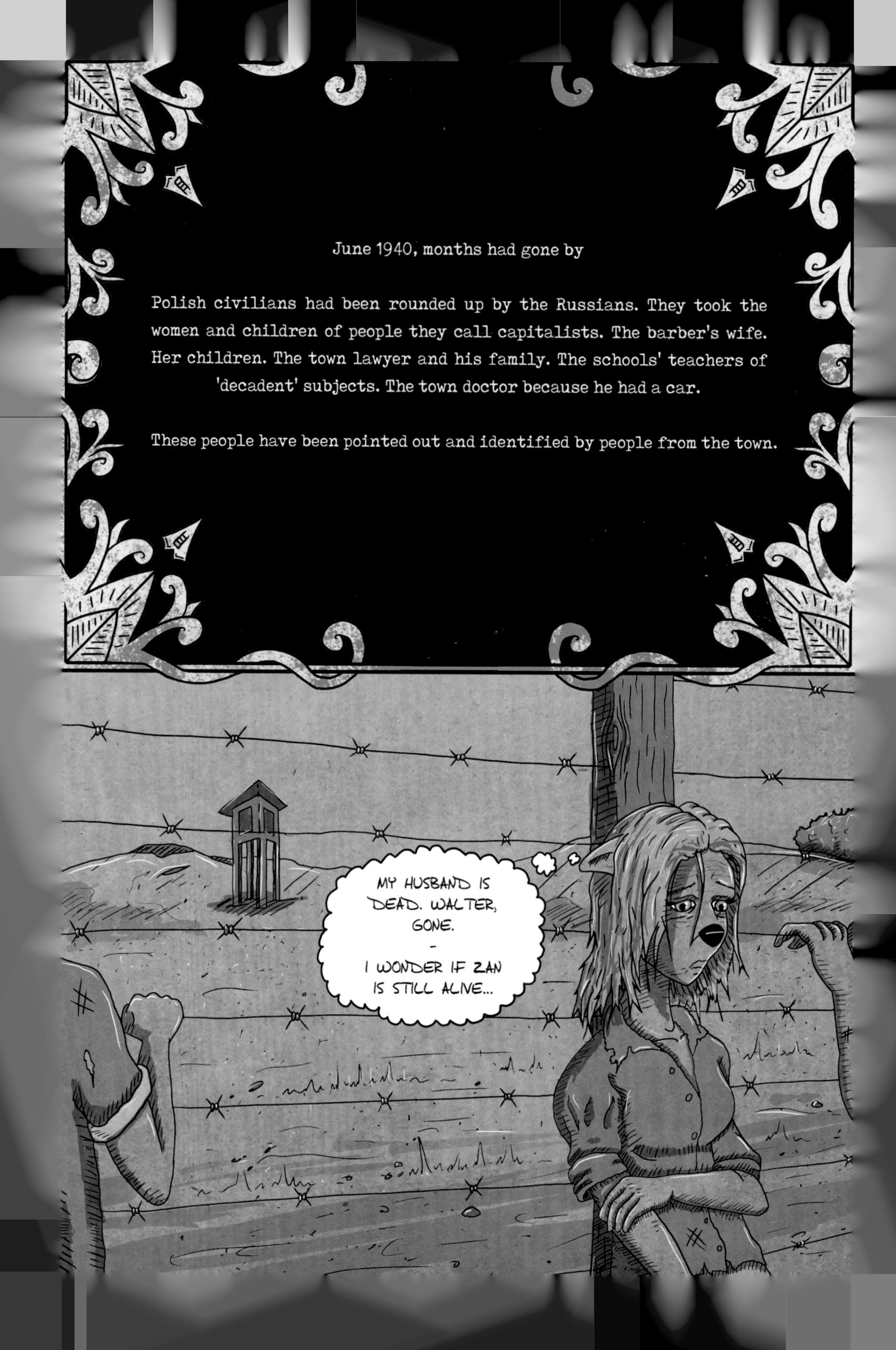
June 1940, months had gone by
Polish civilians had been rounded up by the Russians. They took the women and children of people they call capitalists. The barber's wife. Her children. The town lawyer and his family. The schools' teachers of 'decadent' subjects. The town doctor because he had a car.
These people have been pointed out and identified by people from the town.
MY HUSBAND IS DEAD. WALTER, GONE. - I WONDER IF ZAN IS STILL ALIVE...

GET BACK FROM THE FENCE OR WE'LL SHOOT.
THEY THREW ME IN HERE AS A TRAITOR BECAUSE OF WHERE I WAS BORN. I'M NOT EVEN RUSS-
YOU TOO BITCH!
WHACK

AAHHH, YOU'RE THE ONE FROM UKRAINE
I COULD SHOOT YOU NOW. CAPITALIST DOG.
PFOOOT
SPLAT!!
HOLDYNSKI, DOMAGALSKI, KOSTECKI, ZAN, COME HERE!
YOU CAN'T SEND US FROM OUR HOMES. WHY ARE YOU DOING THIS!?
WE'RE SENDING YOU TO MOTHER RUSSIA
YOU ARE GOING TO BE RE-EDUCATED. TO CURE YOU OF YOUR PETTY BOURGEOIS THOUGHTS
TO LEARN HOW TO BE GOOD CITIZENS
TO BE... - SOVIETS.

GET ON THE TRAIN. THERE IS A BEAUTIFUL PLACE WE ARE SENDING YOU TO ON THE SHORES OF THE BLACK SEA. YOU WILL WITNESS THE BENEFITS OF MOTHER RUSSIA

BUT...

THESE ARE LIVESTOCK CARRAIGES

I'M NEVER GOING TO SEE MY BOYS AGAIN
OFF TO YOUR NICE HOLIDAY CAMP...

HAHAHA
HAHAHA

UNE 1940,
USSIAN-OCCUPI
EAST POLAND

IT'S MY FIRST MISSION AND I'M SCARED...

YOU'RE A CITY GIRL, AREN'T YOU?

AND YOU'RE JEWISH.

...DON'T TELL THE OTHERS PLEASE...

WHY SHOULD I TELL ANYONE. PASS ME THE BAG

WHAT'S IN IT, SIR?

DON'T CALL ME SIR, JEWISH GIRL, AND DON'T DROP THE BAG.
CAREFUL...
THE TRAIN IS COMING

YOU MUST BE BAD LUCK, JEWISH GIRL. THE FUSE WON'T GO TOGETHER
GET BACK INTO THE WOODS
NO I WILL STAND BY YOUR SIDE. YOU GIVE ME COURAGE
CHOOKA
CHOOKA
CHOOK

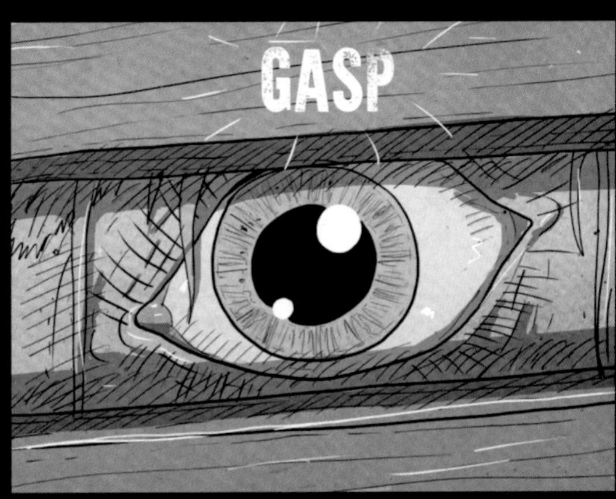
GASP

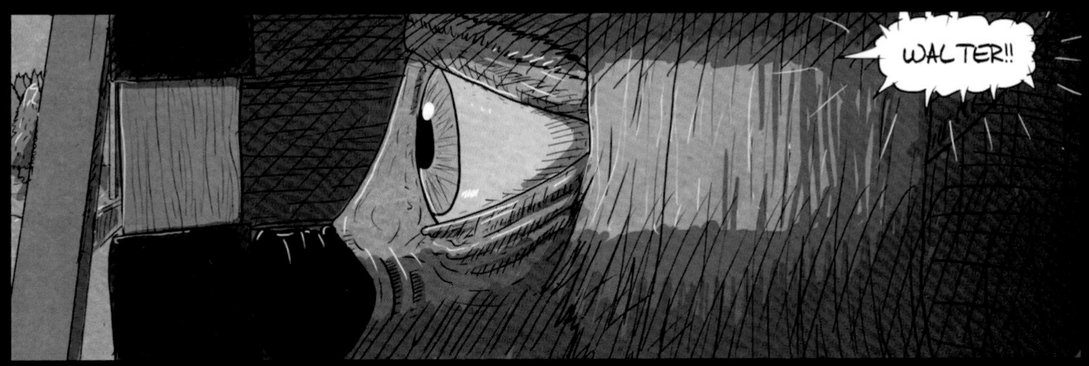
WALTER!!

MY BOY IS STILL ALIVE...

THERE IS HOPE FOR MY COUNTRY.

Heading for Last Hope Island

S.S. HOUND
After going up to Iceland to avoid German U-boats the ship heads South East

shake-shake

England - Last Hope Island!

The port of Liverpool.

The Women's Institute awaits

COME ASHORE, THE LADIES HAVE PREPARED YOU DRINKS AND BUNS
Awright Larry, I'll go for the one on the left... you take the right

HERE YOU ARE DEAR
THANK YOU...

GO ON ZAN, GIVE HER A KISS FOR YOUR COUNTRY

SHOVE

SMOOCH!
mmmmm moist

UHH, SORRY...

THANKS FOR THE COFFEE
IT'S TEA DEARIE, COME BACK FOR MORE XXX

The Polish officer in charge avoids an international incident

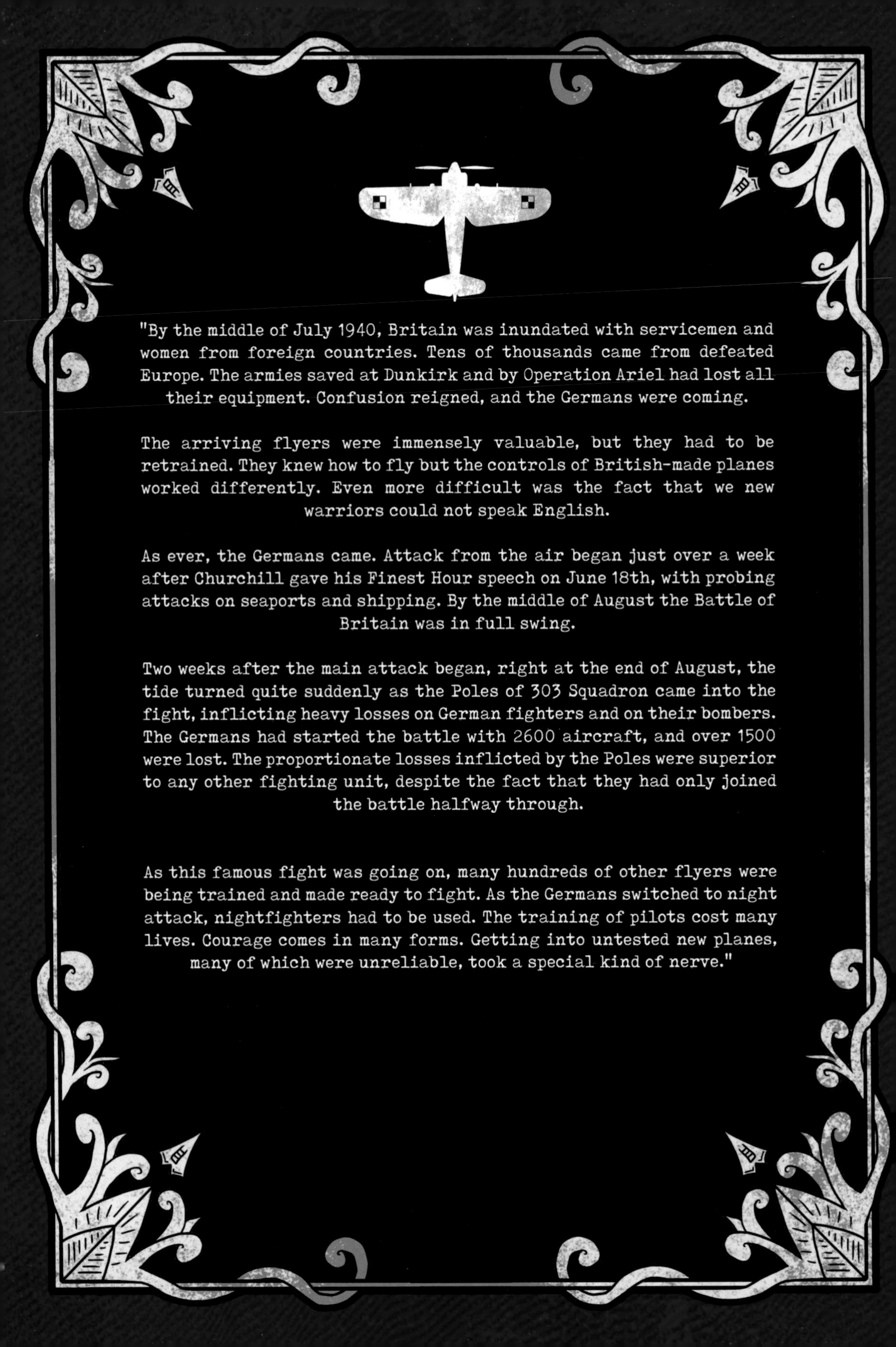

"By the middle of July 1940, Britain was inundated with servicemen and women from foreign countries. Tens of thousands came from defeated Europe. The armies saved at Dunkirk and by Operation Ariel had lost all their equipment. Confusion reigned, and the Germans were coming.

The arriving flyers were immensely valuable, but they had to be retrained. They knew how to fly but the controls of British-made planes worked differently. Even more difficult was the fact that we new warriors could not speak English.

As ever, the Germans came. Attack from the air began just over a week after Churchill gave his Finest Hour speech on June 18th, with probing attacks on seaports and shipping. By the middle of August the Battle of Britain was in full swing.

Two weeks after the main attack began, right at the end of August, the tide turned quite suddenly as the Poles of 303 Squadron came into the fight, inflicting heavy losses on German fighters and on their bombers. The Germans had started the battle with 2600 aircraft, and over 1500 were lost. The proportionate losses inflicted by the Poles were superior to any other fighting unit, despite the fact that they had only joined the battle halfway through.

As this famous fight was going on, many hundreds of other flyers were being trained and made ready to fight. As the Germans switched to night attack, nightfighters had to be used. The training of pilots cost many lives. Courage comes in many forms. Getting into untested new planes, many of which were unreliable, took a special kind of nerve."

APRIL 1941, AFTER MONTHS OF TRAINING
YOU.
YOU.
YOU.
GO TO 308 SQUADRON. REPORT TO CHICHESTER AIRBASE.
I was in a lineup of pilots being assigned to new squadrons

ZAN, YOU'VE BEEN MADE SERGEANT AND YOU'RE GOING TO 307 SQUADRON IN EXETER

YOU'LL BE FLYING IN THE DARK...

CHEERS PETE!
I HOPE WE SEE EACH OTHER AGAIN
FIGHT ON!

WE'RE SPLIT UP. I WONDER IF ANYONE I KNOW WILL BE THERE?

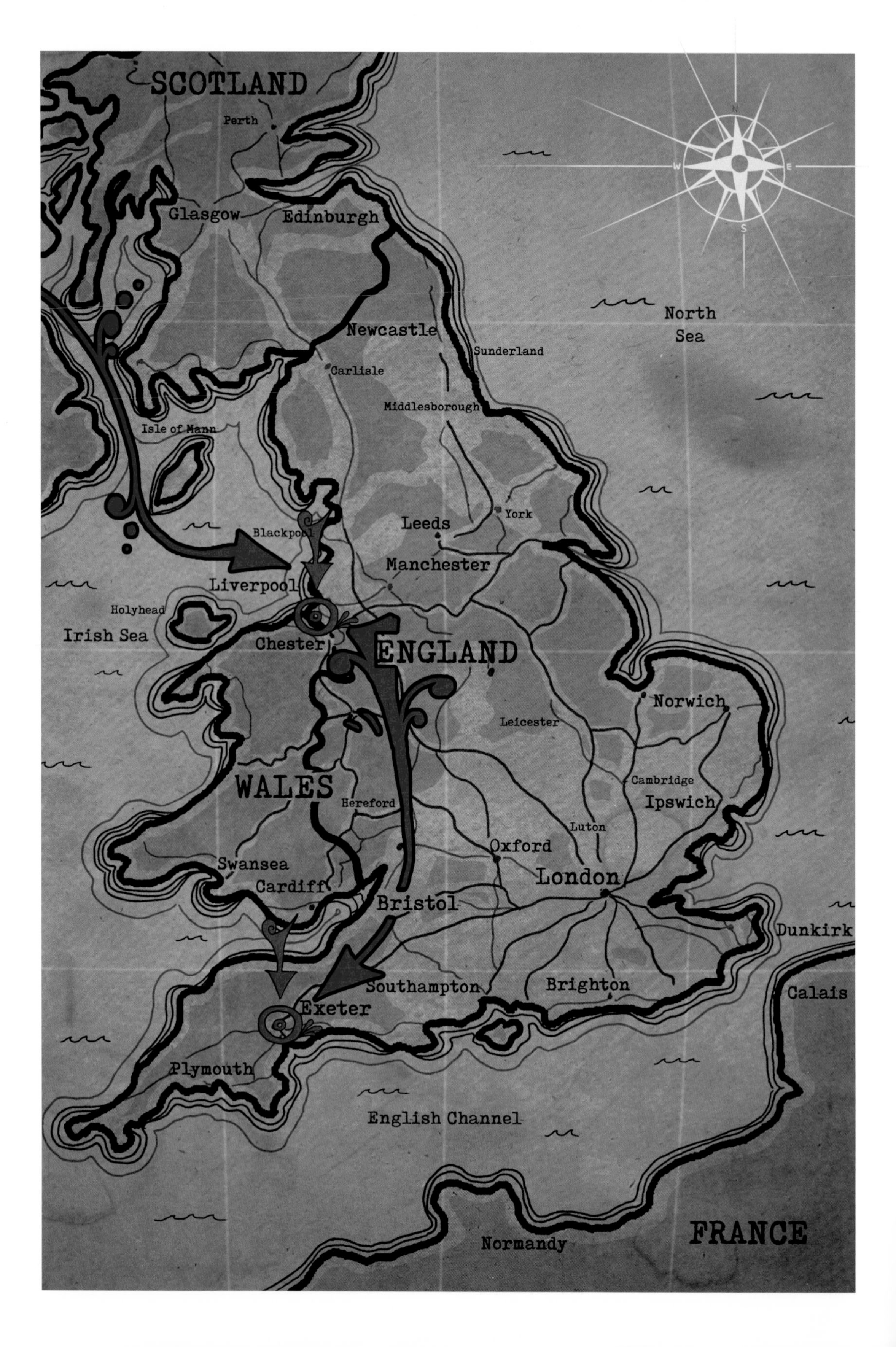

SCOTLAND
Perth
Glasgow
Edinburgh
N
W
E
S
North Sea
Newcastle
Sunderland
Carlisle
Middlesborough
Isle of Mann
York
Leeds
Blackpool
Manchester
Liverpool
Holyhead
Irish Sea
Chester
ENGLAND
Norwich
Leicester
WALES
Cambridge
Ipswich
Hereford
Luton
Oxford
Swansea
London
Cardiff
Bristol
Dunkirk
Southampton
Brighton
Calais
Exeter
Plymouth
English Channel
FRANCE
Normandy

Exeter St Davids Station

A Bolton Paul Nightfighter

A new friend

A FEW DAYS LATER, AT THE 307 BASE IN EXETER

A mysterious figure arrived

WHAM!
SO HERE I AM. COME TO SAVE BRITAIN AND THEY TREAT ME LIKE THIS. AND THEY HAVE KEPT ME STILL AS KORPORAL EVEN THOUGH, LIKE ALL POLES, I AM A HERO.
THIS IS THE FAULT OF THAT IDIOT ZAN! THEY MADE HIM SERGEANT AND HE THINKS I'M A COWARD...

MY PENSION WILL NOT GROW... I WILL BE OLD AND POOR

AT LEAST THERE IS SOME PAPERWORK TO DO

SQUADRON
TRANSFER FORM
PLACE PHOTO HERE
PILOT NAME :
DATE OF BIRTH :
AIRBASE :
SQUADRON :
HMMMM...

...GLUPEK IS STARTING TO HAVE CLEVER PLANS IN HIS HEAD. CLEVER PLANS, YES, YES! I WILL FIX SGT ZAN FOREVER! HAHAHAHA YES, CLEVER GLUPEK...

JUNE 1941,
THE NIGHT SKIES
ABOVE EXETER

CAN YOU SEE ANYTHING, ZAKROCKI?

VVRRRRRRRRRRRRRRRRR

YOU HAVE TO LOOK OUT FOR THE ENEMY'S EXHAUST FLARES

MAYBE. UP THREE HUNDRED FEET...

VVRRRRRRRRRRRRRRRRR

NOPE. DOWN TWO HUNDRED FEET

I AM MISERABLE, FAR FROM HOME AND IT'S HARD TO STAY AWAKE
WHY ARE WE DOING THIS? 
BECAUSE THEY CROSSED A LINE DRAWN ON A MAP, BUT ON THE OTHER SIDE OF THAT LINE WAS OUR COUNTRY...

KKKRRRRRTTT

BANDITS HEADED FOR THE RIVER!
ALL UNITS TO VECTOR SIX

I CAN SEE EXHAUST FLARES!

UP FIVE HUNDRED FEET...

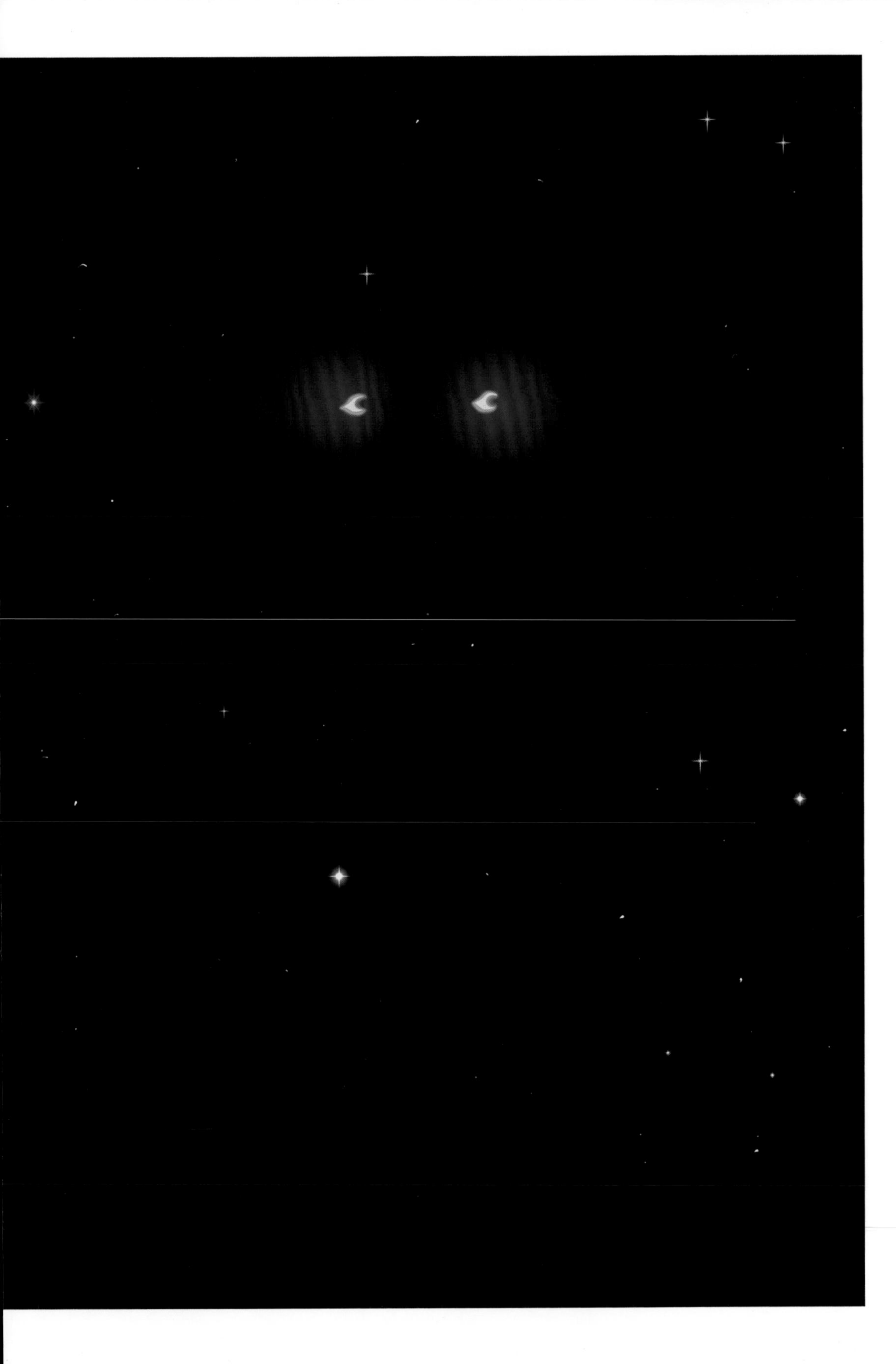

2012,
THE BEACH IN AFRICA
NIGHT HAS FALLEN
THIS DAY IS OVER. I AM TIRED NOW.
Café
A father speaks to his son

YOU'RE NOT GOING TO TELL ME WHAT HAPPENED WITH THE GERMAN PLANES?
NEXT TIME. YOU CAN SEE I SURVIVED

BUT WHAT ABOUT WALTER? AND WHAT DID GLUPEK DO?
WALTER'S GIRL WAS A CHILD OF WAR AND GLUPEK CAUSED TROUBLE, BUT ONLY FOR ME
AND YOUR MOTHER SOPHIE?

SIGH
AND YOU HAVEN'T EVEN GOT TO DOE YET.

NEXT TIME...
AND THE AMERICAN? YOU SAID...
YES, YES, I KNOW. NEXT TIME...

TO BE CONTINUED...

SPYDOGS

VOLUME 2 IN THE DOGFIGHT SERIES

THE STORY CONTINUES...